SOME S(
EMBRACE

(NEW WRITING SCOTLAND 15)

Edited by

KATHLEEN JAMIE
and
DONNY O'ROURKE

with Rody Gorman (Gaelic Adviser)

Association for Scottish Literary Studies

Association for Scottish Literary Studies
c/o Department of Scottish History, 9 University Gardens
University of Glasgow, Glasgow G12 8QH

First published 1997

British Library Cataloguing in Publication Data

A CIP record for this book is available
from the British Library

ISBN 0–948877–33–2

Typeset by Roger Booth Associates, Hassocks, West Sussex

Printed by Bell & Bain, Glasgow

CONTENTS

INTRODUCTION

All sorts of embraces are to be found in this year's sampling of recent Scottish writing and they occur in settings as diverse as a resort hotel in Spain, an ex-pat's colony in Abu Dhabi, a Scottish settlement in nineteenth century New Zealand and a castaway's desert island. Of course, there is contemporary Scotland in all its copious complexity, from slices of urban lives, to the acid dream of a Pict (just one of the Pictish inflected pieces in the book). There's exciting work here in each of Scotland's languages, and in many of its dialects. *New Writing Scotland*'s long-standing capacity to attract excellent translations into Scots remains an attractive feature of the series. Asian writers make a considerable mark this year and there is nothing merely 'correct' about the prominence of their work here, nor about the much larger proportion of gay writing published this time. Poetry and fiction by women are much in evidence. The reworking of 'A Drunk Man Looks At The Thistle', by and from the perspective of a woman, celebrates that impressive and eclectic profusion.

We didn't have to strain to achieve balance; outstanding work by all kinds of writers from all kinds of places teemed in by the sackful so that we've mixed selections from distinguished contributors with pieces by writers just beginning to achieve success. Some very promising debuts in print are made in the 1997 anthology.

Some Sort Of Embrace is sad and funny, deadpan and fantastical, obsessive and insouciant; and the volume encompasses an extraordinary range of voices with assured, revealing, unforgettable things to say. Very good work by very good writers had to be left out to get the book down to a manageable size. A collection half as long again could easily have been justified on every ground but cost. Only by saying 'No' to some established writers who have graced previous editions of *NWS*, could we clear the space for new talent to emerge. We are sure they will be back soon.

An annual anthology such as this one can't hope to be all embracing but there was sufficient verve and variety in the submissions to make the editors' task a pleasurably vexing one. So much for 'Never apologise, never complain'! Every poem and story gathered here continues to give us pleasure. We hope you will enjoy embracing the new in Scottish prose and poetry. And if you are a writer intending to send in work for next year's selection PLEASE be realistic about the quantity of poems you submit and about the length of prose pieces likely to find room in a book as pressed for space as this one.

Kathleen Jamie
Donny O'Rourke

NEW WRITING SCOTLAND 16

Submissions are invited for the sixteenth annual volume of *New Writing Scotland,* to be published in 1998, from writers resident in Scotland or Scots by birth or upbringing. Poetry, drama, short fiction or other creative prose may be submitted but not full-length plays or novels, though self-contained extracts are acceptable. The work must be neither previously published nor accepted for publication and may be in any of the languages of Scotland.

Submissions should be typed on one side of the paper only and the sheets secured at the top-left corner. Each individual work should be clearly marked with the author's name and address.

Submissions should be accompanied by two stamped addressed envelopes, with sufficient postage (one for a receipt, the other for return of MSS) and sent by **31 January 1998 (not before November 1997)** to:

Catherine Mc Inerney
Managing Editor, NWS
ASLS
c/o Dept of Scottish History
9 University Gardens
University of Glasgow
Glasgow G12 8QH
Tel: 0141 330 5309

Ken Angus

AIRLIG REVISITED

Memory has a strange and happy knack
   of fixing in their time-warp childhood hours,
and seemingly, whenever I look back,
   everything's magnified by several powers.
I defended our keep, shot arrows from its walls,
   withstood besieging Saracens, slew dragons,
polished my armour, feasted in panelled halls,
   roasted whole oxen, quaffed red wine from flagons.
I braved the rapids, fished for salmon, tracked
   fierce Bengal tigers in the woods, contrived
to swim the shark-infested loch, attacked
   marauding Indians, fought with bears, survived.

Sixty years on, I find when I return
        a tiny bungalow, a copse, a burn.

SUNSET AT ORMAIG

We meet at the march dyke: he with soap and a can of hot
water, I with my instruments and gown. The sun, a hazy
blood-red ball, smoulders above the Paps of Jura. Wet
peat sucks at our boots, and all around we sense the tang
of crushed bog-myrtle.

   Like a sudden mirage, a rush-fringed lochan looms. At
the edge of the dark water a new-calved heifer lies forlorn;
smeared with blood and ordure, the dark flesh of her
prolapsed womb stretches behind her. A living cloak of
midges rises from the recumbent beast, engulfs, gnaws,
torments us; our very eyeballs seethe with collective venom.

   The light cannot wait. Ignoring the crawling pests, we
see to her swiftly, tenderly. The womb in place, we prop
her on her breast. She drinks fitfully from the shallows.

   A thin red rim of dying sun peeps behind Jura. We
stride back through the twilight, letting the cool balm of
the myrtle soothe our faces. My companion, chatting
freely, swings his can in a jaunty hand, the moon in her
white petticoat riding on his shoulder.

Meg Bateman

SAN OIFIS

Uair is a-rithist
slìogaidh m' aire air falbh,
is greasaidh mi na dèidh,
ga leadairt is ga h-earalachadh,
gus an till sinn a dh'iomain
nam facal dhan chrò.

Ach bidh an cìobair air cus fhaicinn
's e ruith a' choin
is chan fhada mus déan e fead ris
an treud fhàgail ach an toir iad na stùcannan orra;
bidh na solais a' dol air mus till iad
dhan chompiùtair air mo bheulaibh.

IN THE OFFICE

Time and again
my attention slips away,
and I hurry after it,
cursing and exhorting it,
till we return to driving
the words to the pen.

But the shepherd will have seen too much
chasing after the dog
and before long he whistles to it
to leave the flock and make for the peaks;
the lights will be going on before they return
to the computer in front of me.

'S DÒCHA NACH MOTHAICHEADH CUID

nach tusa an t-aon fhear feusagach
tha ag ithe còmhla rium an-diugh,
is mi coimhead a cheart cho suigeartach
's a bha mi bho chionn seachdain.

'S e cuid dhem dhìobhail nach gabh an deifir
a chur an cèill a th' eadar thu fhèin 's fir eile.

PROBABLY SOME WOULD NOT NOTICE

that you are not the same bearded man
as is eating with me today,
especially as I'm looking
no less animated than last week.

It is part of my pain that I cannot express
that difference between other men and yourself.

CHAN EIL RUDAN CHO TROM

Chan eil rudan cho trom
air an neach a dh'fhalbhas –
bidh fiaradh eile aig a' ghrèin,
bidh mùthadh na chomas...
Chan amhlaigh dhan neach a dh'fhanas
is gach oisean san t-sràid na chuimhneachan,
doras gach taigh-seinns' na chlach-chinn
dhan toileachas-inntinn a chaidh seachad.

THINGS ARE NOT SO HARD

Things are not so hard
on the one who leaves –
the light will have a different slant,
change will be possible...
It's not the same for the one who remains,
with every street corner a memorial,
every pub-door a head-stone
to that excitement that has passed.

Paul Brownsey

SOME SORT OF EMBRACE

'God pairs kippers.' I used to know someone for whom that was the complete explanation of every romance. However surprising or incomprehensible the coupling appeared from the outside – 'Tom Harkin and *Julia Cloudsley*?' – Elaine's point was that there must have been some deep divided-halves-of-the-same-soul affinity that made their pairing the most natural thing in the world. But that was over twenty years ago.

Whether she would have said it today of Kenneth Gribble and his Michael may be doubted. Each, you would think, simply bargained with the other on the basis of the goods he brought to the market and the other's need of them. Isn't it an orthodoxy in 'relationship counselling' that people only stay in a relationship because they each get a profit that outweighs their inevitable loss?

… Kenneth Gribble was a Couldnae. By this was meant, in the gay bars of Glasgow, 'I couldnae do it with him to save my life.' His face, in which the cheeks bulged downwards and seemed in danger of obliterating the tiny over-delicate mouth, was now getting lined with resentful disappointment… but it would be a mistake to continue with a physical description because someone else with the same body might have found a niche, friends, a right to a sex-life. Kenneth Gribble's Couldnae status came from qualities of soul: his body exuded limp sour hopelessness, and his words and eyes clung as though to leech substance from you.

I had not noticed him in the bar and his greeting made me feel he had crept up on me.

'Oh, hello, Kenneth.' Not Ken, for the abbreviation might imply friendship; least of all Kenny, with its suggestion of regular-guy likeability. 'How's the beautiful Michael?' The question was his dole, not intended to initiate a conversation, for it did you no good to be seen talking to Kenneth Couldnae. Indeed, the question gave him more than his due, for it might seem to legitimise his pathetic hopeless pretence to fancy the unattainable Michael.

'Well, there's nothing to be expected, is there? I try to make sure he eats properly and has all the stress taken off him, and of course he gets worse.'

'*I try to make sure...*' – I would not let him see my aston-
ishment.

'Well, it was the only chance I was going to get, wasn't it?
He's ill. He can't work. He's got no money. So I chose my
moment and put it to him: if he'd come and live with me I'd
look after him as long as he needed it. Lived. It wasn't a flat-
share I had in mind, I made that clear. I love him, so I get what
I want, don't I?

'It's all false, of course. Couldn't be anything else, could it?
Like this Christmas he wants.

'He was supposed to be helping me clear out my mother's
place after she went into the home. Of course he couldn't do
anything but sit and watch. Still, to be watched by someone
like him who's yours – can't be bad, can it? There were all these
Christmas things – a big plastic tree, artificial lights, tinsel,
shiny balls and things. Used to be the only sort of balls I got to
handle.'

A smirking invitation from Kenneth Gribble to share
double entendres was disgusting.

'I was going to throw it all out but he said, couldn't we have
a Christmas? In September. Because he mightn't be alive in
December. So that's what we're doing. Christmas dinner on
September 25th. You're invited. You've got to send a card and
bring a present, and it's got to be wrapped in Christmas paper.
Quality paper, too, not the thin stuff you can see through from
the street traders in Sauchiehall Street, ten sheets for fifty pee.
It's going to be the full thing. Everything to keep up the illusion.'

He sighed in imitation of the way normal people sigh
about things.

... Very beautiful people tend to be friendly. Maybe this is a
big tease, leading you on. More likely, they take it for granted
you realise they are out of your league and you won't miscon-
strue their attention to you. Or perhaps their beauty means
merely that they have no reason not to be pleasant. Certainly
Michael's look and words of welcome as I entered the bar
could have meant I was just the person he was hoping to see.

'Christmas is coming and the geese are getting fat,' I said,
this being September 16th. There was something I wanted to
know and the challenge of finding it out from Michael excited
me.

'I'm not, though.' Having smiled to put me at my ease he
looked down at himself, and his legs inside his denims made you

think of a wee boy trying on his father's clothes. 'Still, this is one of my good days, so Kenny dropped me off here for an hour.'

I ventured: 'Kenneth Couldnae.'

His dreamy tone said that he had not even heard me. 'Sometimes I can't believe my luck. He's one of the good guys, Kenny.'

'Except that he exacts his price, from what he goes around saying.'

Michael's perplexed look was on my behalf rather than his own, as though he could not quite see what was the confusion from which he was politely ready to rescue me.

'I think if I'd been in your place I'd have found it hard... well, no, it *wouldn't* have been hard, that's precisely it... I'd have found it difficult to give him what he wanted.'

How enormously it mattered to him, said his look, to understand and benefit from whatever I was trying to say. I was encouraged to spell it out.

'Sex. With Kenneth Gribble. Good guy, good body, it doesn't follow.'

Michael thought about this and then spoke very carefully, as though he'd suddenly had to give a talk about an unfamiliar subject like hydraulics or chaos theory. 'I don't think you feel like that about it, Paul, if sex means an awful lot to you.' His voice respectful: no reproof intended.

Would that have seemed a stunning insight if he had not been so beautiful? Sometimes your eyes are engorged by a face or a body and you are entirely lost to yourself, but a moment later you can look away unscathed and forgetful because you saw meanness of spirit in the narrowing of a forehead or delight that was brutish in an unguarded grin at someone else. I looked to see whether Michael's willingness to set up home with Kenneth Gribble was reflected in a cowardly thinning of the cheeks about the mouth or puffy resignation below the eyes, but there was no such flaw in his beauty. The way his short fair hair clung to the back of his head guaranteed absolute integrity.

'And it does, to you?' I itched to say, not daring.

... On September 25th I had Christmas dinner at Kenneth Gribble's little flat in a damp-feeling close where the tang of disinfectant did not quite hide an earthy smell of something unpleasant. There was a holly wreath on the front door, neighbour-defying, world-defying. Michael's touch, that must be.

Indoors the illusion of Christmas was complete: decorations, tree, cards in which people had written normal things

like, 'Have a great Xmas'. The curtains were drawn and the
lights were on as though it were dark December, not the bright
daylight of 4 pm in September.

There were crackers on the table, expensive 'luxury' ones,
and a centrepiece of a brass angel made to twirl by the rising
heat from two red candles. Kenneth had cooked the full works:
turkey and cranberry sauce and Christmas pudding and brandy
sauce. There was nothing at all wrong with it. The competence
disconcerted. So did his manner, for he combined a self-congrat-
ulatory *tarantara!* delight in laying good things before us with a
sort of sour insistence on the hollowness of the whole event.

Fortunately it was one of Michael's good days. He could
manage a little of everything, though not much of anything.
When he went quiet for a few minutes, Kenneth said, 'One of
your little low moments. Remember, it will pass. So will the
good moments.'

There were only two guests besides me, Iain and Wolfgang,
a couple.

'Well, most people go home to their families at this time of
year, don't they?' Kenneth explained, and I thought to myself,
'Or have better things to do than spend Christmas with
Kenneth Couldnae,' only then realising what he had said.

Wolfgang had met Iain in a sauna in Vienna, instantly
declared he loved him, and followed him back to Glasgow. He
was boisterously enthusiastic about every dish, every fresh
stroke of the festivities, and delighted in the elaborate paper
hats from the crackers, which resembled Napoleonic tricorns.
But it came to seem he thought the purpose of the event was to
welcome him to Glasgow.

Kenneth said to Iain, 'Well at least *he* thinks he's wanted.
No lack of self-esteem *there*, is there?' and Iain, his voice fraught
with having worryingly many things to tell Wolfgang, said
rather sharply, 'It's in honour of Michael, Wolfgang. I told you.'

'Ah yes, but so many things you tell me and to learn them
all I try is difficult. Honour of Michael!' He raised his glass,
stretching a long arm upwards to its fullest extent. 'Why we
honour of Michael?'

'He's going to die.' Kenneth.

Michael spoke to Kenneth rather than to the company,
gently. 'But now my life means an awful lot to me.' He was
raised above us by a cushion, because there was so little flesh
on him that a hard chair hurt.

'And where that place Michael is going is, in Scotland or Britain?'

Iain's glasses doubly reflected the twirling angel.

The sound reached us before we realised what it was: children's voices singing. We made out words: '...bright sky look'd down where He lay, The little Lord Jesus asleep...' The sentimentality engulfed us and our surprise. We smiled at each other with absolutely unfeigned affection.

Anxiously Iain took a twenty-pound note from his wallet. 'Give them this.'

The carol-singers were Kenneth's brother's two wee boys and two of their friends. When we had seen them off, and also Iain and Wolfgang, Iain seeming to welcome the carol-singers' interruption as an opportunity to take his lover away, I asked Kenneth how he had explained the carol-singing business to his brother – to the boys, too.

'I told them the truth.' Unfortunately, Kenneth Gribble was wide from the hips down and he held his body with a stiffness that dissociated it from whatever he said, so the words did not resonate with courage at all.

I went to the loo. On my way back to the kitchen I was halted in my tracks as I passed the open door of the sitting-room. In the darkness the only illumination came from the garish lights snaked around the artificial tree. But half-hidden in the false green foliage these reds and blues and ambers were magic jewels in a fairyland forest. Shiny glittery globes and strands of tinsel caught gleams. One ball turned, spun, with mysterious slowness and peace. Parcels shadowy beneath the tree contained everything your heart desired. A truce had been accomplished. You could believe that an old promise was suddenly renewed, out of time, out of season, by means in themselves tawdry and contemptible. No doubt I was merely experiencing the reactivation of some safe childhood memory in, let's face it, emotional circumstances – isn't all we feel just the reactivation of buried childhood memories? Still I could not help a kind of reverence softening my step. I prepared a witty parodic summation of the matter: 'Extraordinary how potent cheap trinkets are.'

My quietened tread meant that my return to the kitchen was unexpected, and as I opened the door there was a scuffling noise. I realised I had interrupted some sort of embrace which they were too mannerly to maintain in my presence.

10

Larry Butler

I come with big white flowers
snow white hair wearing galoshes
hot smiles raring to kiss everything

Bowlegged I swagger across the room
dribbling on the carpet

You gently touch my shoulder

Holy   Unhinged   Standard Lamp!

My tea leaves come true
the cat counts the chickens
before they hatch   You are my ground

coffee   weetabix   biscuits and oh
won't you please

just gorgeous the geranium

Stewart Conn

FACES

Features easy to visualise
on Quattrocento canvases:

his the gaze of a Giorgione
shepherd-boy, that girl's poise

pure Botticelli. Elsewhere
Raphael skin-tones. An expectancy

I'd all but given up on.
The train jolting to a standstill,

they reclaim backpacks
and sleeping-bags, jump down

and cross the leafy platform
to the Rowardennan bus.

*

Visiting the Rijksmuseum
not on honeymoon

but in our early years,
we spent hours

intercepting the glances
of Rembrandt self-portraits.

I identified then
with the younger man

but now on the wane
recall that American's

high-pitched squeal of glee:
'Gee, they're all the same guy!'

*

We carried home two collages
we couldn't choose between, and sat them

side by side in the front room
for an agreed few days' pondering.

One grew on us – till we saw in it
a shape like Andy Capp in his flat hat.

Once outed, hard to ignore.
We took the other. From that day on

it has helped (I hope) keep my feet
on the ground. As soon as I get notions

above my station, I hear someone shout
'Hey: a wee man in a skip bunnet!'.

*

Like burnt iron but more fragile,
bits having flaked off since

my half-hearted haggling;
the stall-owner offering

little provenance, beyond
'spirit-mask, ancient and tribal'.

Less reassuring than malign:
snoutish nostrils, the mouth

agape, no saying what it might
ward off or induce. Through its

pepperpot sockets, the view seen
alarmingly similar to my own.

Katrina Crosbie

NO SPLASH

They're all there: Mother, Father Kenneth, Sister Mary James. A row of disembodied heads, lined up along the curtain rail like coconuts in a shy. Mother is wearing her chapel hat, the grey felt with the three wilted cherries on the brim.

I pull your scarlet shirt off, tugging the cuffs down over the knobs of your wrists.

Your eyes flicker towards the door then back again. It's your first season as a waiter. You've never fucked a guest before, have you?

You can't be more than seventeen.

I suck your left nipple, softly at first then harder, making it stand out like a woman's.

I smell of sex. Deep, musky, exotic as incense, mingling with the sour salty scent of you.

The sun glares at me.

Wait, I say.

I walk over to the hessian curtains that line the glass balcony-wall, look upwards.

The heads have gone.

I close the curtains, damping down the squeals and splashes from the pool, the rattles and thumps of the Flamenco display in the terrace bar.

You shift from one foot to the other, watch silently as I take off my tangerine bikini top. You don't speak much English. You don't have to. Your erection tells me everything I need to know. I step out of my bikini pants, naked apart from the heavy gold crucifix that Mother gave me for my first Communion.

I want to keep that on.

Ah, that brought her back. And the rest of the coconuts. Look at them. Look at Sister Mary James with her shrivelled lips screwed shut. I can still hear her, though, her voice like the rustle of dead leaves, just the way it was when I was fourteen: Remember girls, you may think you've found Heaven on earth with a man. That's fine. Just don't expect to get there in the hereafter.

Smug as Moses on the Mount, knowing we'd fall for it, knowing her withered womb and dried-up old orifices gave her the right to tell us how to live our lives.

To hell with her. You're naked and we're on the bed, only the suction of sweat between us. You lick my ear, take it in your mouth. Your tongue is hot and wet. My inner thighs are sticky with my own wetness.

I press my mouth into the hollow of your collar-bone. You taste of herring and pickles. I want to eat you, gobble you up. No – not gobble. Slowly. Slowly, slowly, slowly –

That's what Mother used to say. Slowly, Ellen. Don't bolt your food, Ellen. Chew each mouthful a hundred times. Take your time, or you won't get the benefit.

Don't look at boys, Ellen. Don't let them kiss you. Don't look at yourself naked. Don't sit on your father's knee in short skirts. Don't touch yourself down there.

No wonder Father left. There must have been as many don'ts for him.

But you were right about one thing, Mother. Come on, don't be shy. Look.

Slowly *is* best.

See what a good girl I am, Mother?

Outside the Flamenco dancers are reaching a climax, stamping and shouting and drumming their heels on the wooden stage.

Inside there's only our synchronised breath, the slap of damp skin on skin, the squeak of latex as you roll the contraceptive onto your cock. The unfocused, dreamy look in your eyes as you ease my thighs apart. Then you're kneeling over me, stroking me there, teasing me, tickling me, then you open me up with your fingers and my stomach starts somersaulting, *don't lose your nerve, Ellen, this is it*, then there's a man's cock inside me where nothing's ever been before, not fingers, not even a Tampax because that would have sent me straight to hell.

But once you're in it's easy. Instinct tells me how to move, how to follow you as though we were dancing.

I clutch your back, wrap my legs around you and – Oh, I'm sorry, Father Kenneth. I'd forgotten you were there. Look, Father, let me show you what it's like.

You must have wondered what it would be like to touch a woman's body, Father. I mean *really* touch a woman's body, not the way you used to touch me after Bible class, hands trembling with the thrill of it, mouthing, What a clever girl you are, Ellen, nobody else knows their Catechism like you do, and me knowing what was coming next, trying to concentrate on the sweet honey-fragrance of the polish that they used in the vestry, *if I can keep smelling that it'll be alright*, but it wasn't, it was your sharp whisky breath, and the peppermint smell of the Polos you used to suck, and it was the fear fluttering in my gut, fear and something else that I didn't recognise at twelve, it was your finger sliding down my buttocks and in between, rubbing against my blue-and-white striped cotton dress and serge pants. And it was knowing I could never tell Mother because a priest can do no wrong, Ellen. Do as Father Kenneth tells you, Ellen. Comb your hair back off your face, Ellen; we have to keep ourselves nice for Father Kenneth.

You never tried to go inside, did you, Father? I would have respected you more if you had. Hated you, but respected you. Even at that age I knew that a man should be more than a bag of wasted spunk.

Wait, Father Kenneth... where are you going? Have I said something wrong?

It doesn't matter.

Back to you, my darling, my sweet Spanish angel.

In and out, in and out, your balls banging against me with each thrust, full and heavy as two ripe plums. Crusts of drying saliva on my cheeks, my neck, my forehead. Somebody's winding up a watch-spring in my groin, it's getting tighter and tighter, we're panting like animals now, clawing and nipping and growling and OH GOD the crucifix biting into my breast-bone. Did it hurt you too, darling? Pleasure and pain, pleasure and pain ah Mother, you were right, one leads to the other but which comes first, and then we *are* coming, both of us.

And they're all lined up in the grandstand, goggling at us as we go for the racing finish. Mother's mouth puckered as though she's been sucking lemons, Father Kenneth with his tongue hanging out, looking as if he's been caught playing with himself, Sister Mary James wrinkling her nose as if somebody's stuck a dog turd in her face.

Madre de Dios, you gasp. I spur my heels into the backs of your thighs then JESUS never mind the watch-spring, the whole fucking watch explodes.

You twitch inside me like a landed salmon as your cock subsides.

You sleep.

I stand on the balcony wrapped in a beach towel, all bright

reds and greens and yellows. I've showered, but already I feel the prickle of sweat on my neck, my breasts, the inside of my elbows.

I'm thinking about Mother. Mother lying in white-silk-lined state with too much face powder on. Father Kenneth in full regalia, the tears on his cheeks echoing the rain on the stained glass as he sends her on her way. And still that whiff of complicity between them.

Poor Father Kenneth, all alone now we're both gone.

I think about another day, in the solicitor's office.

I think about sunshine, red wine, tangerine bikinis. Spain, France, Italy.

The relief is like coming all over again.

I go into the room and take a bottle of San Miguel from the mini-bar. On the way back I glance up at the curtain rail.

All I can see is dust.

On the balcony I unfasten the crucifix. Drawing my arm back I throw hard in the direction of the swimming pool, watch the arc of gold slice through blue then disappear.

I listen for the splash, but hear nothing.

Anne Donovan

DEAR SANTA

Ma mammy disnae love me. Ah kin see it in her eyes, no the way she looks at me, but the way she looks through me, the way you look at sumpn that's been in the hoose fur years; you know it's there but you don't see it. It's hard no tae be seen, it makes you wee and crumpled up inside. When ah kiss her on the cheek her skin creases, soft and squashy lik a marshmallow, and close up ah see the lines runnin doon the sidey her mooth and smell the powder on her face. She doesny kiss me back.

You kin read fur ten minutes but then that light's tae be aff.
Gonny come and tuck me in, mammy?
You're too big tae be tucked in.
She keeps watchin the television.
You tuck Katie in.
Katie's only five. You're a big girl.
Ah'm eight year auld. Ah'm a big girl.

Ah don't know if ma mammy loved me afore Katie wis born, ah canny mind that far back but ah must of been jealous when she was wee. Ah remember wan day she wis lyin sleepin in her pram ootside and ah got plastercine and made it intae wee balls and stuck them all ower her face; she looked as if she had some horrible disease. Ah mind staunin there lookin doon at that soft skin covered in sticky horrible purple lumps and felt good inside, warm and full.

Katie's asleep in the other bed, fair curly hair spread oot across the pillow, smilin in her sleep the way she does when she's awake. Ma sister is perfect, ah kin see that, she's wee and pretty and aye happy, bubblin ower wi life. When the sun shines she's runnin aboot the gairden efter sunbeams and when it rains she pits on her wellies and splashes in the puddles. She never cries. Ma daddy says she's a princess, her teacher says she's an angel, ma mammy says

Why can't you be more like your sister?

In the school nativity play Katie gets picked as the angel that tells Mary she's gonty huv the baby Jesus so ma mammy sits up all night sewin her a white robe and a perra golden wings. Ah'm a shepherd, wi a stripy tea towel roon ma heid. In the photy she's at the front, in between Mary and Joseph, glitterin as if she really wis an angel, and ah'm this big lurkin thing

at the endy the back row, daurk and blurred. The photy gets
framed and put on the unit in the livin room.

Thon's a lovely photy.

*Katie's pure beautiful in that frock. She looks just lik an
angel.*

And Alison's gettin awful big fur her age.

*Ah know, ah kin haurdly get anythin tae fit her. Ah hud tae
pit panels intae her communion frock so she could wear it fur
her confirmation and it's less than a year auld.*

It's Christmas Eve, the shops sparkle and we're in
Debenham's queuein up tae see Santa. Ah don't think ah
believe in Santa any mair but don't want tae admit it. Katie
goes first and sits on his knee and tells him she wants a baby
doll and a cot. Then she gies him a big kiss, slides doon fae his
knee and runs towards ma daddy.

Santa says if ah'm a good girl ah'll get it, daddy.

She pits her airms roon his neck and he birls her, wee legs
stickin oot fae unner her frock.

You're aye a good girl, princess.

He smiles at me.

On ye go, hen.

Close up ah kin see Santa's beard is fake. The glue has
dried on his skin and there's wee rolled-up rubbery bits on his
cheek. But his knee feels solid tae sit on, and when he smiles
the lines crinkle roon his blue eyes.

And what's your name, pet?

Alison.

Whit age are you, Alison?

Eight.

*You're a big girl for eight, aren't you? And whit dae you
want for Christmas, Alison?*

Ah knew he wisnae Santa, no the real Santa that lived in
Greenland wi the reindeer, if there is a real Santa anyway, but
his eyes were kind and he called me by ma name and ah wanted
to tell him, ah tried tae tell him.

Ah want ma mammy tae...

But then a big lump cam up, no in ma throat, but in ma
hert, heavy and grey lik a stane, that stopped me fae sayin it.

You want your mammy? Is she no here?

He looked roon fur help as though he wis feart ah wis
gonny cry and he didny want a greetin wean on his knee. Ah
shook ma heid. He looked straight intae ma face.

Whit dae you want fae Santa, Alison?
Ah don't know… ah know but ah canny say.
Is it a secret?
Aye.
Ah tell you whit. Why don't you write it doon and… do
you have a chimney at home?
No a real wan, it's a gas fire.
Well you put the letter in a secret place, and I'll find it.
And if you're a good girl, you'll get what you want.
Ah'm a good girl.

Christmas Eve ah'm sittin on the bed in ma pyjamas wia pad of blue lined paper and a biro. The room is daurk but the wee bedside lamp makes a white circle that lights up the page ah'm starin at. It's hard tae find the words.

Dear Santa,
Please could you
I would like
If it's no too much bother

But what is it ah'm tryin tae say? Could you make ma mammy love me? That's no Santa's job, he's there tae gie oot sweeties and toys tae weans wanst a year, so there's nae point in askin him. If there is a Santa. Ah look oot the windae; the sky's dirty grey and ah don't think we'll huv a white Christmas somehow.

The door opens and ma mammy comes in. The hall light's on and her fair hair sticks oot all roon her heid, fuzzy and soft. A canny see her face.

Are you no asleep yet? It's nine o'clock.

Ah'm writin ma letter tae Santa.

Santa doesny come if yer no sleepin. Look there's Katie, sound.

She bends over Katie's bed, where she's lying wi wan airm stickin oot fae under the covers. Ma mammy lifts the bed-clothes ower her, then turns tae me.

Hurry up and finish that letter, Alison. Ah'll pit it in fronty the fire and Santa'll get it when he comes.

Ma mammy sits on the bed beside me while ah take a clean bit of paper and write dead slow so its ma best writin.

Dear Santa,
Please could i have a Sindy doll and a toy dog. I am a good girl.

Love
Alison

Ah fold the paper twice, print SANTA on the front, then gie it tae ma mammy She pits it in her pocket and lifts the covers fur me tae get inside. Ah coorie doon, watchin her hair glowin like a halo against the blackness of the room. Ah love strokin her hair, it's that soft and fuzzy but she canny be bothered wi that and jerks her heid away, sayin *don't, you'll mess it up*, just lik she does when ma daddy tries tae touch it. But it's that quiet and still and she's in a good mood so ah lift ma haun and touch her hair, just a wee bit.

Mammy, how come you've got fair hair and Katie's got fair hair and mines is broon?

You take efter yer daddy and Katie takes efter me.

Ah wisht ah had fair hair.

How? There's nothin wrang wi broon hair.

Ah wisht ah had hair lik yours.

Ma mammy smiles and the lines roon her eyes get deeper but she looks at me mair soft like.

Go tae sleep hen or Santa'll no come.

She bends ower and kisses me, a dry kiss, barely grazin ma cheek, and before ah have time tae kiss her back she's switched off the bedside light, stood up and moved tae the door.

Night Alison.

Night mammy.

She goes oot, nearly closin the door, but leavin a wee crack of light fallin across the bedclothes.

Moira Duff

MOBILE PHONE AT THE DANGEROUS JOIN
BETWEEN CARRIAGES

Someone deals the floor between the carriages
like a pack of cards. Four men

get on at Darlington and stand in this travelling ante-room
while two neurotic steel and glass doors

hyperventilate with indecision. Four heads
over Beethoven's 5th of the sleepers

whip around and change direction
like a board of bagatelle. One phones

his wife as a girl comes up. Light shines
on her nose and cheeks and she keeps on saying

'Sorry?' then laughing like trodden-on Chinese
rice boxes. Then the one who phoned yells out

'Fiona! – I am NOT a homosexual!' At which
squashed aluminium foil

quadruples down the packed carriage.

Bill Duncan

ACID DREAM OF A PICT

Beyond us lies no nation;
nothing but waves and rocks.

Calgacus

Tae a clift in an ootlie scarp in the gloom,
through a clabber o glaur in the smirr
eh crept half-deid, pechin an droukit
til ah lay doon alane in the mirk.

The blash o the sea lulled dull in ma heid
but the puddock-stools lichted ma mind.
Syne doverin ower in deleerit dreams
came Past, Noo an Ayont o ma kind.

A door in the dark tae the mid o ma skull
bleestered wide an lat through veezions fey:
the thunner loud rummelt, the fire-flaucht bleezed bricht.
(In ma heid or ootside? Hard tae say.)

Fae sheddas tae bleeze, fae skimmer tae derk
like yon stroboscopes causin a trance;
whiles aa roond the clift, fae the flair tae the ruif,
sworlin haar, like dry ice at a dance.

Spirals an chevrons an knotwork an baists;
psychedelia wiz boarn in this cave.
A great birlin swirl, primeval an hip;
Pictish stanes richt through tae nineties rave.

Shimmerin Z-rods an zoomorphic forms,
peintit burds in fluorescent day-glo.
Is this the sixties, or am eh at a rave
wi the ultimate, faur-oot licht show?

Cup an ring markins an skeerie designs;
acid rainbows flicked licht ower ma face.
Patterns sae eldricht a gift gied tae me –
the marks o the airt o ma race.

An in sic strange scenes in this film in ma mind
starred an antrin an bamboozlin cast;
the Boar o Dores, the Bull o Burgheid
lowpin, vivid 'tween Future an Past.

Laivin sic dreams, weird, uncanny as thae
an altered man, much changed, a New Me,
wi upheeze an smeddum an spreerit tae share,
showed the folk o ma tribe hoo tae see.

Whiles 'bodies tattooed in strange designs'
we carved stanes, warked in siller an bronze
'Living in tents, unclothed and unshod',
wrought mysteries unkent wi oor haunds.

Whigmaleeries an stanes an jowels an claes
fae a 'Painted and Brutish North Tribe'
whaas instinct tae ornament drew a line straicht
tae the wonders o Book o Kells' scribes.

Noo Pictish an Celtic are Nineties High Style –
Shooglenify an Tribal Techno,
Capercaillie an Afro-Celt aw lead richt back
tae us peinted anes fae lang ago.

Bi the time eh hud waukened an craaled oot the cave
the morn-blink glimmed in the lift.
The chittrin o burds soondit perfect an new
as I waandered hame, wi ma strange gift.

Oor stanemen made wonders wi symbols an signs
aa through Pictland, fae Orkney tae Fife;
things o airt, antrin, wi secrets untelt,
monuments tae oor tribe's life.

There's little that's left noo tae tell o the Picts;
the carved stanes speak some history,
the 'Pit' o wir place names in the North an the East,
but the story's nine-tenths mystery.

Ither peoples hae wizards an shamans an priests;
the Pictish tribe somehoo got me
tae see veezions an dreams on the waas o a cave
an hallucinate oor destiny.

Gerrie Fellows

from *The Promissory Notes*

A WOMAN ABSENT FROM THE MUSEUM
MUSES ON HER LIFE IN SOUTH DUNEDIN

Those of us whom no one thought to photograph
are here as ghosts   to give the lie
to bread without scarceness   freedom by
honest toil   our lungs choked with the motes
of our sewing, its fibres wound around our throats
and lives: a narrative of nights
without coals to keep the grate alight
of eyes sunk into pouches of skin and sleep
of fingers bound by need to the incessant needle

No new world   No paradise
a grime smeared house where damp clung
to the weatherboards   a valley where smoke hung
all year above a clanking factory
and yet we dreamt   of wonderful simplicities:
fresh vegetables in a cottage garden
a geranium on a window sill   and everything clean
We dreamt   for dreaming's free, nothing
could stop us   of what we had been promised
of what bread without scarceness might have meant

THE COLONY OF OTAGO REVEALED TO
THE ELECT

From the ends of the earth we gave thanks to the Lord
for the dream vouchsafed us of a Christian settlement
its streets and kirks, its places of learning
concentrated and contiguous   upright, the working model
of a market town   its inhabitants tradespeople
artisans   earning a living by honest toil

But we were hollow, restless   The life gnawed at us
North of the Waitaki the Anglicans were making money

We turned our backs on the inhuman tracts of the hills
the whisperings beyond   That way was emptiness
illusion   and no life for a pillar of the Kirk

Isolated there men lost communion with their own kind
forsook Sunday worship   became idolators of land
and money   fell under its spell in glittering waters
rivers of ice   Their eyes betrayed them
lost to the murmuring country of the imagination
her bush choked gulches and winter passes

And the worshippers of the land rode out   and struggled with
speargrass and matagouri   and breaking through the watershed set
fire to the scrub that they might drive sheep over the passes   And
they laid claim to the living earth and parcelled out the footsteps of
those who had gone before them.

AN ANNOTATION TO THE ACCOUNT
BY CHARLES KETTLE, SURVEYOR

On convulsed green I set my grid: a formal end
to the hapless filth of the old world   Dunedin
was to be a town fit for a godly experiment

The ships dropped anchor to avenues multiplied
as cleanly as equations   Princes Street was divided
by tree stumps, tussock transected my pattern of pegs
I was abused for my tardiness by folk who had no notion
of the intricacies of the surveyor's art
his tribulations in such terrain as this

I insisted on straightness but the land would not obey me
(even in my dreams it dipped   wayward and irrational)
By day it rose up   buckled against my thoroughfares
My streets hung over gulches, curved into steps   but I
pressed onward   instructed, with theodolite and wooden rule
to build New Edinburgh   a footprint inked indelibly
across the contours   order and rectitude

Raymond Friel

SUNDAY NIGHTS
for Janet

Ensconced in the Percy
While veteran colleagues
Hoisted their *Guardians*,
We wafted back in late
For afternoon lessons,
Indulgent and smiley;
Then one day we didn't
And by tea-time (the news
Intro blaring ignored)
Were true friends of Dennis –
Seven years in the Scrubs
For manslaughter, his wife
Charged *that day* with thieving.
He burned on a roller-
coaster ride to the edge,
Smoke pouring from black wings…
Latching on (God knows why),
He kept re-appearing
With trinities of pints,
Growling intensely through
'The River' – *now I act*
Like I don't remember…
His L-O-V-E first beating time
On the table; 'If ever
You need a hand,' he said,
'You let me know…' and dug
A thumb into my neck.
'YOU HEAR ME?' While he wept
Rebel songs at the bar,
We swigged from a few pints
And took off down the Grove.
Our love was on the wing…

Courtship in riotous
Weekend pubs and last trains –
Having driven ourselves
For six months, not wishing
To appear the staid one –
Wasn't our scene; instead
I fine-tuned my chilli
For Sunday nights (adding
A spoon of brown sugar
To the moreish simmer),
Glass of merlot to hand
And maybe Van the Man.
Easy on each other
In our house of pictures,
We learned to open up
And just *say* what it was,
While your acerbic wit
Punctured my ludicrous
Boy sensitivities.
But the young girl's nightmares
Persisted in the bride –
Incorrigible id
Pictured us mouth to mouth,
Toe to toe, cobwebbed in
A narcoleptic tomb;
Morning-ness of perfume
And Breakfast TV
Not enough to dispel
The fear that clung to you.

The traumas of labour
And difficult first months
With our boy recede now.
What stayed with me almost
As much was how, leaving
Hospital with Jamie
Swinging in the car seat,
When that man held open
The door, sore as you were,
You quickened your step
To relieve him of it,
And *then* I could've cried.
(Was that Yeats's pity
Beyond all telling
Hid in the heart of love?)
A long torrid summer
Cools into September
And our favourite season.
More used to who we are,
We wait for chiller air
And darkness unafraid;
With all the help we've got.

Robin Fulton

NOTES ON THE LAWS OF NATURE

I

Pines on the hill
chaotically interpret
the north wind. They brush against me
with raw silence.

II

Twelve blind windows
scrutinise me. That empty house
adds to itself one more cubit
of emptiness.

III

Monteverdi
abrades me with his present tense
his loud golden ignorance of
four centuries.

WAITING TO CROSS A FJORD

Birches and pines have come down their long slopes.
They are squat and hazy. They swell and shrink.

Underwater stones are too visible.
They don't give a hint of sunless valleys.

Rain. Small rings hurry into each other.
There are so many of them they die young.

There is much of life in a backwater.
From here the wide fjord surface is opaque

as stone. An assurance. Sea-level is
the safest of places, height- and depth-free.

The ferry rounds a point. Prow and stern high,
a slice of melon shape balancing like

a junk or miniature idea of junk
in an old print, undaunted by ink waves.

I am daunted now, here at sea-level
for the opaque surface turns translucent

and sunlight can be seen losing itself.
The unseen valleys are truly sunless.

Time that has been running and running stops.
Birches and pines have loped to their true heights.

SOMETHING STUBBORN

I saw the universe
seethe like a herring shoal,
fish-backs fighting for space
in space without limits.
With nowhere to cross to
or from my panic at
the absence of stepping
stones bridges ferry boats
was ... unnecessary.
Then I saw the edges
of the universe, rough
hacked wooden beams holding
the All in its place. Then
the universe shrank and
shrank. Soon it was a large
black spot in the blue sky
then microscopic then
too small for microscopes.
Something stubborn remained.
I couldn't stop staring
at it the way we gaze
at where we think a lark
is hidden in clear air.

W.N. Herbert

JACOBITE'S LADDER

Once I dreamt that my head was a stone
shoved beneath a throne in London,
and that a troop of kings and queens
in progressively cleaner regalia
came and sat on my head
for a period of years,
breaking their royal wind in my ear.

As I lay stifled there, I saw
a ladder stretching from the top of the Law Hill
into the soup-flecked clouds,
and climbing up and down this blue ladder
were a series of patriots, some historical,
some fictional: all more real
than the town spluttering beneath them,
at least to the monarchs, who shifted
their faith-defending buttocks
uncomfortably throughout.

There were the renowned Pictish heroes:
Drost of the hundred battles; Brude,
son of Pontius Pilate; and Nechtan,
slayer of mere Northumbrians, all
wearing unknown costumes and recounting
unknowable legends.
There were the triumvirate of television, stage and screen:
Wallace, Bruce and Scottish Play, all
preceded by their faithful definite articles.
There were the terrible Caledonian twins: North
and the Shepherd, Burns and McGonagall,
Louis and Stevenson; and there
were the tribe of Trocchi, all
of whom drank of the waters of Leith and acquired
the power of literary amnesia. That's right:
they didn't know they were born.

Then I was wrestling with Big Tam
dressed as a galley slave
and as we fought he whispered
the history of the golf ball in my other ear:
'Wooden, feathery, Haskell.'
And when he got to gutta-percha
I nutted him with my stony pow,
and as he fell he muttered,
'You'll never get to Marbella
with a swing like that.'

Then I was the hammer Mjollnir
driving spikes into the blue palms of the sky,
nailing a saltire of jet-trails into place
over Cambuslang. There was writing on
my temples, words cut into the stone,
but I found no-one who could read them, nor
could I find a mirror, and yet I knew
these were my land's commandments.
When I awoke, I named the place
where I had rested 'Stonehaven'
and journeyed on my way rejoicing
beneath a great pyramid of cloud.

SONG OF THE STRANGER IN A BROWN PUB

Eh jist came in here fur thi bathroom
Eh jist came here tae use thi loo;
Eh don't waant tae speak to nae fuckers
and therr's no way Eh'm talkin tae you.

Eh jist came in here fur a swally
and mebbe a double or two;
Eh don't waant tae breed wi your collie
or interface now with your shoe.

Meh nostrils do not waant expandin,
meh dick disnae need a tattoo –
Eh'm as shair that yir girlfriend's a stottir,
as yir colon's shair it's a kazoo.

The time has come when Eh must leave ye,
Yir acquaintance Eh shall not renew;
Eh'm jist aff tae cuckold and thieve ye
while you sit in here and yahoo.

Harvey Holton

THE CITY O KIRKS
Gleann da Lough

Here amin the brackin an aik
whaur tourists like masell trauchle
the place maun hae bin hailly.
Afore they hardy men o god
stertit their biggin:
afore the city o kirks shone
in the licht o the muckle glen:
afore Kevin made his bed
an biggit the beehive cell
that drew disciples frae awe airts
tae be near his awe fuu hailliness
there maun hae bin the reek
o stinkhorn risin roond an haurd
as the tooer
saftend ainly bi the virgins
warm cathedral
whaur men worshipt an prayed
amin watter an rock
hewin stane an mortar.
Nae aik leaf or strae for a roof
but solid biggit stane
tae peak in the lift for
the ain god oot o the mony
they maun hae kent.
The roads weel troddin these days
as it aye maun hae bin:
the simmers sin aye splits the stanes
an tea an scones are wir offerin
for the wine an breid
the bluid an heids
that we think are wir ain.
Calm the lochs oan a simmers day,
sweet the reek o comein rain,
fire burns the inmaist pairts
aik an birk sing in the wund.

A.B. Jackson

ON MARYHILL ROAD

19A Milngavie   1 min
19A Correction   2 min

Electronic bus-stop display

I will wait the extra minute
and go to Correction
where sweetpeas grow upright
on the lawns of Eden

where light-adjusted children
play safe in the dark
all sugar no medicine
their games unelectric

where groups of identical pig
make perfect bacon
by the compound of thin men
with no shoes on

I will wait the extra minute
and go to Correction
to catch the unwavering scent
of brimstone

Nasim Marie Jafry

SWIMMING LESSONS

When Margaret woke up she wanted to go swimming. She hadn't been to the baths for years.

In Abu Dhabi you never went to the baths. You swam at the Holiday Inn or at the British Club or in the sea. She'd been there for four years. She'd gone with Ian when he got an engineering contract. She'd got a nursing job in a renal unit really easily.

Margaret left Abu Dhabi because she was tired. She was tired of the easiness of it all.

A few months ago a crowd of them had gone out for Martin's thirtieth birthday. Martin was a geologist, Ian's closest ex-pat friend. Martin shared a flat with Erik, the Norwegian engineer. They'd all gone out and got wasted on Cosmopolitans. A cocktail of vodka, gin, lime and cranberry juice. They were lethal.

The bar was right on the beach. Someone had suggested going swimming. They'd all gone in with their clothes on. Margaret was wearing a t-shirt dress and leggings. The dress kept ballooning up over her head, so she'd taken it off and swum in her underwear. She'd let go of the dress, giggling.

Erik rescued the garment and manoeuvred into it, the wet cotton sticking to his thick body. Don't you dare rip that, she screamed at him. Everyone was squealing and laughing. Margaret thought Erik suited the red and white print with his green eyes and his tan. The bar-man shouted at them to come in, that they were making too much noise.

They'd all walked home together, shivering and dripping and laughing. Drunk ex-pats behaving like the kind of people Margaret couldn't be bothered with. It's a wonder they weren't all arrested. When no-one was looking Margaret and Erik sneaked into an alley and kissed. Margaret enjoyed it, but she told Erik it could never happen again. Ian went to Martin's for a night-cap, and Erik walked Margaret the rest of the way home.

She invited him in for coffee and told him it could never happen again.

There was something unreal about ex-pat life where you did things you didn't really mean to. It was all that sun.

She'd seen photos of Erik's wife and kids. They all looked
so happy and healthy and Scandinavian. Erik worked eight
weeks on and two weeks off. His wife missed him.

Margaret was tired of always having a tan; tired of the
endless duty-free; tired of the other ex-pats, especially the kind
who'd been waving their Union Jacks down at the beach the
time the Tories got back in.

She was tired of seeing Filipinos and Indians and Africans
treated badly. She had never got used to having a maid. She'd
tried to become friends with Irma, but Irma remained shy and
subservient, stuck in her role. Margaret insisted on doing her
own hand-washing and got angry with Ian when he com-
plained that Irma had ruined *another* shirt of his in the wash.
Irma was beautiful. She was Samoan. Margaret wondered if
Ian had ever slept with her.

She was tired of the wailing from the mosques; tired of
never waking up to the rain battering the windows.

She'd been with Ian for seven years, since her twenty-first.
They'd worn fake wedding rings in Abu Dhabi so that they
could live together without arousing suspicion. She knew he'd
been screwing the Filipino secretary for months. When she'd
asked him, he'd denied it, but she really didn't mind. Not now.

It was pissing down the day she landed back at Glasgow
airport. Everything looked grey. Margaret was smiling as she
got off the plane.

She had enough savings to keep her going until she got
another job. She had good references and could always get
temporary nursing work. Margaret was sometimes struck by
the irony of earning her living from other people's bad kidneys.

She stayed with her mother for a couple of weeks before
moving into a flat in Anniesland. Three hundred and fifty
pounds a month. She'd been away so long she didn't know if
that was good or bad. She got great sunsets from the kitchen.

This morning, the sixth morning in her new flat, she'd
woken up dying to go swimming. She called the baths to see if
they were open. She couldn't remember if they gave you towels
or not. She packed a Dubai Sheraton beach towel and her
Clinique soap and shampoo. She had enough Clinique products to stock Frasers in Buchanan Street. Margaret wasn't
extravagant, but she liked good skin-care. Erik had stolen the
towel from the hotel the time they'd gone to Dubai.

She got a bus on Great Western Road even though it was

just a couple of stops to the baths. It was a novelty being on an orange Glasgow bus. She liked being amongst other Glaswegians. Everyone looked poor. The third world immigrant workers in Abu Dhabi had looked poor too, but it had been a different kind of poverty.

The smell of the chlorine hit her as soon as she walked in. She bought her ticket and went through the turnstile. It was one of those old-fashioned pools where the changing rooms and showers are built round the pool. It made you think of the Romans. She got changed and put her fifty pence in the locker. She pinned the key to her swimsuit. It was a black one-piece with purple cross-over straps. She knew she looked good in it. She walked downstairs to the turquoise water.

There were three lanes. One section for school kids, and two for the other swimmers. The serious swimmers swam up and down relentlessly in the middle lane. Margaret got into the serious lane and did twenty lengths. She stopped up at the deep end and watched the kids in the first lane. They looked like primary sevens. They were lined up shivering at the side of the pool, taking turns at diving in. The boys were mostly skinny. Some of the girls were chubby and had corned-beef legs. The gym teacher looked worn out.

Margaret thought about the time in primary five she'd dived into the wee pool and got concussion from banging her head at the bottom. The pool attendant had saved her and given her a McCowans caramel for being brave. The teacher had given her a row on the mini-bus on the way back to school. She'd called her a stupid little girl for diving into the wee pool.

When you were at school and the teachers were horrible to you, you thought it was because they hated you. You didn't know it was because they had a shite home-life and hated their husbands.

Margaret moved into the non-serious lane and hooked her ankles under the bar. She floated on her back, letting the pool gurgle into her ears. She could see the coke and crisps machines out of the corner of her eye. That had always been her favourite part of the swimming lessons. The can of coke and the cheese and onion ringos. She loved the heaviness of the coke can as it fell out of the machine. Then you'd go back to school and your hair wouldn't be dry properly all day, and you'd still smell of chlorine when you got home.

She lay there floating with her random thoughts.

She'd just got in from school and thrown her school-bag on the kitchen floor. 'Mum, mum, guess what, I know what a pun is! *I never eat scones so late, they make me so dis-con-so-late.* That's a pun!' Margaret had stopped talking when she saw her mother, the joy of her pun instantly drowned. 'Mummy, why are you crying, what happened to your head?!' 'It's okay, pet, it's nothing. Go and get changed for the Brownies before tea.' 'But I always get changed *after* tea. *Did daddy do that, did daddy hit you again, did daddy cut your head?!'* Margaret heard her own ten year old voice screaming through the water and the chlorine. She could see her Brownie uniform with the green emblem and the ink-stained pocket. She'd been a Pixie.

She ducked under the divider and went back to the serious lane. She did another ten lengths. She wanted more thoughts, so she hooked up to the side again.

Floating, gurgling, lapping.

Now she could see Erik naked and grinning on the bed in the Dubai Sheraton. He'd told her in Norwegian that she had beautiful breasts. He'd made her come with his tongue. Ian had never been able to do that.

He came in her mouth, groaning so loudly she thought she'd hurt him. She ran to the toilet and spat out his sperm. She knew that you could get AIDS from oral sex if you had lesions in your mouth. It was a grey area. Margaret didn't like grey areas: she liked black and white.

They'd had a shower together and lain on the bed in their white towelling hotel dressing gowns. He told her about how camel-racers kidnapped young children from India to use as jockeys, and how they made them wear Velcro trousers to stop them from falling off the camels. Margaret didn't believe him. Ask Martin, he's got photos, Erik said before dosing off. Margaret started to cry in spite of herself.

They played at the *Minister's Cat* on the drive back to Abu Dhabi. The *minister's cat's an adulterous, bad, clinical cat.* They didn't get beyond *r.* Erik pretended to go in the huff because he didn't know what *rastafarian* meant. They had to stop once so that Margaret could pee.

She had held the moment in her head: crouched, peeing behind the dunes at the side of the motor way, the sand still hot even though it was evening, a married Norwegian waiting for her in the jeep. They got back to Abu Dhabi in time for her farewell party which Martin had arranged against her wishes. She didn't want to say good-bye to a crowd of people she didn't even like. Everyone knew that Erik had driven her to Dubai for a last duty-free splurge. Everyone knew, but nobody cared.

She did one more length and got out of the pool.

The showers were communal. She felt embarrassed by her Clinique soap in its expensive-looking green case. She shampooed her hair, enjoying the hot spikes of water against her skin.

A couple of school kids had joined her in the showers. They were shoving each other and giggling. She knew they were looking at her *down there*. It had been a while since she had waxed her bikini line and there were a few stray hairs. The giggling got louder and the taller one pushed his friend against her. *He wants to shag you, missus!* They'd run back into the pool before she had time to react. She was mortified and hoped the heat of the shower would hide her blushing. The water went cold before she'd finished rinsing her hair.

She got the rest of her stuff from her locker and dressed quickly. Her teeth were aching from the chlorine. She headed for the snack machines in the foyer. She selected diet pepsi and salt and vinegar crisps. There was no cheese and onion.

When she got back to the flat the second post had come. An airmail envelope with an Abu Dhabi post-mark. The sender's italic hand-writing had been crossed out by Margaret's mother and re-addressed. She must have thought it was from Ian. Her mother had really liked Ian. Margaret put the letter on the kitchen table and had another shower to rinse her hair properly. She rinsed out her swim-suit and hung it up. She knew she was stalling.

She made a cup of black coffee and sat at the kitchen table, fingering the letter. His writing was so neat and Scandinavian. She knew what was in the letter, and she knew that once she'd opened the letter she'd have to make a decision. She knew already what the decision was, but she wanted to delay it.

She was craving a cigarette. She usually only smoked when she was drunk and she only ever smoked menthol. She opened the pack of duty-free she'd got for her cousin, Joanne. Joanne wouldn't mind, not under the circumstances.

She dragged on the cigarette and thought of her other life over there. It was already beginning to seem like a dream. This was real. Sitting in a flat in Glasgow was real. Over there was not real. It was all a big party.

Ian had taken her to the airport. They'd held hands on the drive there. Margaret didn't really want to, but she knew Ian needed the closeness. After checking her cases in, she'd wanted to go straight through to the departure lounge. Ian's eyes were filling up. 'We've had some good times, kid, haven't we?' 'I have to go. Ian, I have to go. Take care of yourself. Make sure Irma gets the envelope I left for her.' 'If you need anything, you know where I am... I love you, Maggie. Don't give up on us.' His desperation was getting to her. She hugged him and didn't look back. She still had a big lump in her throat when the plane took off.

She stubbed out the cigarette. It was making her feel sick, smoking so early in the day. She opened the letter. *Dear beautiful Margaret, I stop in Amsterdam on the way to Norway sixth September. Please come to meet me. I am at the American Hotel. I miss your beautiful Scottish breasts. I want your kisses. From the rastafarian Norwegian.*

She could not get away with his cheekiness. She kissed the letter, embarrassed at herself. She put the kettle on again and sat down. Slowly she tore up the letter and made a wee pile out of the pieces before putting them in the bin with the half-smoked cigarette. She stared out of the window, listening to the kettle. She wished it was evening so that she could watch the sun setting. The whole sky lit up and made her feel calm.

Tomorrow she would go swimming again.

Brian Johnstone

DRY STONE WORK
for Archie

Teamwork, you said and grabbed the corner
of the sack. Too late. My tensing back,
unused like yours, to working with its hands,
went crack, as strain was felt and slack
was taken up. We soldiered on and stones
built thick and fast. Time dribbled past
and you, my senior by a score of years,
worked steadfast hour on hour. I gasped
and, fighting to keep up, the stones became
this wall.

            Now, looking at it all,
you off to more jobs still to do, it seems
a small thing to have made me crawl
from chair to chair, with aching back,
feeling much as stones inside a sack.

EARDLEY IN GLASGOW

She trails a line of kids, a crocodile
of snotty noses, baggy shorts, worn shoes,
a crèche which dogs her steps from mile to mile,
devoted to whatever she might choose.
A battered pushchair cradles all she needs:
a bag of paints, her brushes, palette knives
and canvas, stretched and primed, aching with greed
for line and colour, individual lives.
She sits them on the kerbstones, by the grates
of peeling rooms, in closes, tenements
and paints, a fury to communicate,
to merge material and sentiment.

Her muses watch with unselfconscious eyes
as childhood ages, takes a new disguise.

EARDLEY IN CATTERLINE

She stands in neutral ground, between the tides,
between the showers of hail and sleet she paints.
Her canvas open to the sky, she hides
from nothing, choosing to ignore restraints
that might have stopped the wellspring from within.
A gnawing at her being, more than art
lends her the strength, the power to begin
her struggle with the medium. Her part
is to devote her days to sea and sky,
to storm and wave, to cloud, to weather's hand.
At night she writes of where the moon will lie,
reflections on the water from the land.

And walking from the road on her last trip,
she slows her pace but does not lose her grip.

Murchadh Dòmhnallach

GUILBNEACH

Ged dh'itheadh beul na h-oidhche
Mo nàbaidhean 's mo chàirdean
Tha mi fada nad chomain
A ghuilbnich
Airson gun dhùisg sibh
Amhran balbh nam bhodhaig
A thrusaich mi fhìn le ceòl –
Is còmhladh, choisich sinn a-mach
Dhan an fhionnaraidh.

Murdo MacLeod MacDonald

CURLEW

Though twilight eats
My friends and neighbours
I am much obliged to you
Curlew
For arousing a dormant song
Within me
Which I clothed in music –
And together, we walked out
Into the evening.

AN TOBHTA

Nuair a nochd mi sa chamhanaich
Theich na taibhsean air falbh,
Gam fhàgail an cois nan clachan
A chunnaic murt is marbhadh.
Ach a dh'aindeoin seo
Bha na clachan gan garadh fhèin rium
A chionn 's gun robh mi beò.

THE RUIN

When I appeared at dawn
The ghosts fled,
Leaving me in the stones' company –
Those witnesses to murder and death.
But despite this
The stones warmed themselves against me
As I was alive.

FAOISGNEADH

Mar a' chiad ghealag-làir
A thog a cinn
As deaghaidh rotach a' Gheamhraidh,
'S mar gach beàrnan-brìde grianach
A mhosgail à ròidean bìtheach –
Ròidean cumhang Shamhraidh.

Mar fhaoisgneadh chnothan
Ann an tiormachd an Fhoghair;
Sultmhorachd na Sultaine
Gath grèine tro fhuil
Gun stòineadh an-diugh
Et ceter-a gu et ceter-u.

BURSTING FORTH (OF LIFE)

[You are] Like the first snowdrop
That lifted its head
After Winter's blasts.
Like each sunny dandelion
That wakes from tarry roads –
Narrow Summer roads.

Like an explosion of nuts
In Autumn's aridity;
The abundance of September
A sun-ray through blood
Without rest today
Et ceter-a to et ceter-z.

Ciara MacLaverty

THE BABY-SITTERS

It had happened again. She said the words but they must have come out wrong because she didn't mean it like that. She felt stupid like those contestants on The Generation Game who tried to make pots out of clay but the clay was just flopping all over the place and the people in the audience were laughing their heads off.

'No, I mean I just really like them. They're cool, y'know?' Nicola Radcliffe wasn't convinced.

'Sounds to me like you fancy both of them and you could be a lezzie.'

'I'm not – honest,' said Ruth, hearing her voice plead.

'In fact,' said Nicola, 'I'm gonna shout it out in the playground, unless...'

'Unless what?'

'Unless you give me your dinner money.'

By the time Ruth got home it was dark. When she opened the door she smelled chips – the Friday treat. The kitchen was warm, the windows steamed up.

'There you are love. Tea's a bit early tonight. Your Dad and I are going to a dinner dance thing at the Lochside.'

'Are the baby-sitters coming?'

'Of course. I told them half seven.' Her mother rolled the chips from the wire basket on to the plate.

'Great,' said Ruth looking at her little brother who went on eating his beans with a spoon. She bit a warm chip off the end of her fork, her head tilting in thought.

'But actually Mum, surely I'll soon be old enough to look after *him*.'

'Well, there's a fair difference between eleven and sixteen. Anyway, I thought you liked to see the girls. How many fish fingers?'

'Two please.' She would have to tell her about the dinner money.

'I lost my dinner money again Mum, so it's kinda lucky Dad was there, eh?'

'Lucky for you, you mean,' said her mum.

Ruth had gone to the men's staff room at lunch time,

dreading who would open the door. Worst would have been Smith or McKinley. It was her Dad. He rattled the coins in his trouser pocket and offered her a palm full of change. She selected a fifty pence piece, saying, 'Thanks Dad.'

Her mother looked at the kitchen clock.

'I wonder what's keeping him. I've still to have a bath.'

Ruth shrugged.

'Maybe the teacher mobile broke down.' Her mum rolled her eyes towards the ceiling and then broke into a smile at the last minute.

When the door bell rang Ruth ran to answer it. The baby-sitters were wearing their stripy jackets. Lisa's had brown stripes and Kate's had blue. They always wore the same clothes except in different colours. Ruth could never decide which colour she liked best. She always loved both. The same with their hair. Lisa's was brown and Kate's was blonde. It made her think of white chocolate and ordinary chocolate and she could not choose one above the other.

In the living room her Dad was bent down on his hunkers, poking the fire.

'Come on in here girls and sit down. How are you doing?'

'Fine thanks, Sir,' said the baby-sitters at the same time. Lisa usually talked more than Kate but Kate had a smile that let you know she was always listening. Like she was weighing things up in her head.

'Better not get coal on me posh suit, eh?' he said. They had lived in Scotland since Ruth was a baby but she always forgot how Irish her Dad sounded until he did his boomy teacher voice.

'Nice dickey bow, Sir,' said Lisa.

'It was Ruth's birthday present to me, wasn't it Ruth?'

'Well, mum helped me pay for it.'

'Helped you pay for what?' said her mother, slipping through the door, both hands trying to fasten a pearl necklace at the nape of her neck. She was wearing a black evening dress and perfume wafted in the air behind her.

'Here, let me,' said her father, helping with the necklace. Her mother kept talking.

'Now I hope you girls will be warm enough. I've just tucked Simon in so he should be okay. Ruth can stay up till half nine and if you could fill a hot water bottle for her.'

Going out, her Dad rattled his pockets, checking for keys.
'Don't be having any wild parties when we're gone now.'
The baby-sitters laughed. They were always laughing.
Sometimes just a giggle, other times they bent over and held
their bellies. They talked about having a 'magic laugh'.
'Hey Lisa, what about lunch time in the canteen queue?'
'Aye, it was a magic laugh.'
As soon as the car had gone Lisa switched the stereo on,
tuning the dial in to Radio Luxembourg. Blondie was singing
'Heart of Glass'.
'Fab,' she said, 'I love this song.' She kicked off her shoes
and began dancing on the carpet. Ruth looked at her tight cords
and how her boobs bounced gently beneath her green jumper.
Ruth had no boobs yet and she hated getting changed for PE
when the other girls could see her vest. Nicola Radcliffe would
whisper to her friends, her hand over her mouth and her eyes
slanted towards Ruth. Nicola wore a lacy white bra and called
it her 'over shoulder boulder holder'. She had big freckley ones
like someone's mother would have. Ruth kept leaving the cata-
logue open at the bra section in the hope that her mum might
get the hint. Even a padded one would do. Lisa's boobs weren't
too small or too big. They looked just right.
'Can you teach me to dance like that?' asked Ruth.
'You have to shake your shoulders like this,' said Lisa, 'and
wriggle your hips.' Ruth found it difficult to combine the two
movements and flopped on to the sofa with a forced laugh to
cover her failed attempt.
'You'll get it eventually,' said Kate, smiling.
Lisa sat down cross-legged on the floor.
'Hey,' said Ruth, 'let's have talking time.' She loved it when
the baby-sitters would talk about boys and she could listen and
ask questions. They called them 'hunks' and give them marks
out of ten. Russell Grant was a 'total hunk', at nine out of ten.
Ruth knew Russell Grant because he often stood, smoking a
cigarette on the corner of main street. She was scared when she
had to walk past him, or worse still, ride past on her bike with
the shopping basket on the front.
Sometimes he shouted 'Hey Paddy, is your Dad in the IRA?'
She always took a beamer and never looked at him but she was
secretly pleased that he even bothered to notice her.
She felt safer at the park on Saturday afternoons where her
Dad took the senior boys for Five a Side. She always picked the

swing nearest the muddy pitch and sat astride it like it was a
rocking horse. She rocked casually back and forth, looking out
to sea and flicking her hair from her shoulders. Each time the
shouts got louder she allowed herself to glance back at the
game. Sometimes it was her Dad: 'Atta boy Russell, good tackle,
keep at 'em now.'

'Dy'a know what Lisa was doing last Saturday night,' said
Kate.

'Whaaat?' said Ruth, dragging the word out, like she just
knew it would be something good.

'Only snogging Ricky Grant in the phone box for 35 minutes.' The baby-sitters shrieked with delight.

'But how did you breathe?' asked Ruth. They were trying
not to laugh but their cheeks filled up with air and it came
bursting out anyway. For a moment Ruth felt a ripple of panic
but she sensed that their laugh was a friendly laugh. It wasn't
a Nicola Radcliffe laugh. Quickly she joined in as if she saw
the joke too but she never really found out the answer.

Sometimes there were piles of green school jotters lying
about the house. Ruth liked to look at the names of the fourth
year class and the graffiti on the cover: 'Russell is a hunk' – 'I
love ???' – 'We rule the school'. Ruth had seen the same things
written on the desks at school. During maths once she read
'Teachers are Bastards', scored heavily in grey pencil. She
propped her textbook up so Mr Miller wouldn't see her trying
to erase it with her Snoopy rubber.

The desks in her Dad's classroom were not made of real
wood but of Formica and were harder to vandalise. She had
only been in his class once. Miss Forsyth had flu and her Dad
had to supervise the 1B English class. He had read them a short
story and afterwards he asked if they had any questions. There
was a moment's silence when Ruth could hear the ticking of
the clock above the blackboard. Caroline Roy put her hand up.

'Is it supposed to be a happy ending, Sir?' Ruth heard herself breath out. Afterwards in the blue cloakrooms Gillian
asked her, 'Would you call your Dad 'Sir' or just Dad if he was
our English teacher?'

'Sir, I suppose,' said Ruth.

'Would you go beetroot?'

Ruth shook her head. 'Naw...'

Except for that time at the school disco. Her Dad was help-

ing with the crisps and juice and afterwards Kate and Lisa had
waved him on to the dance floor to a Madness song. They were
wearing their red and blue satin jeans and they looked so cool.
He looked really weird dancing in his suit.

'Your Dad's so cute,' said Lisa afterwards. Ruth thought
only babies and kittens could be cute.

Ruth hadn't got used to the extra time spent travelling to
secondary school. She joined the crowd who waited by the
new post office, silent in the blustery grey mornings. Ricky
Grant and all the big boys sat on the back seat and gave the
'V' sign to the primary kids in the street. Lisa and Kate always
sat together half way up. Ruth sat near the front beside Alison
Miller who bit her nails for most of the journey. The bus was
always quiet in the mornings but on the way home the boys
on the back sang at the top of their voices. To the tune of 'I'd
like to buy the world a Coke', they sang 'I'd like to buy Evans
a rope and hang him from the tree, with Donaldson and Mc
Niven to keep him companee...'. Ruth was so relieved that
they never sang anything about her Dad. At least not so far.
He always got a lift to school with two other teachers in a
wreckedy old van owned by the woodwork teacher. It smelled
of petrol and saw dust and it was the baby-sitters who named
it 'the teacher mobile'.

'We get your Dad for SH now,' said Kate, putting bread into
the toaster.

'What's SH?' asked Ruth. Lisa was pouring the tea.

'Social Health. Haven't you had it yet?' she said. 'It's when
they tell you about the dangers of alcohol.' She said the word
'dangers' in a deep voice. Kate sniggered and said. 'And the
dangers of...'

'Oh yeah we got something like that from Campbell,' Ruth
interrupted. She remembered a slide show in a darkened classroom, the blinds pulled down. There were pictures of glasses of
wine and beer and whisky with units ascribed to them. No one
was paying much attention. Some of the boys were passing
Polo mints beneath the desks. Mr Campbell raised his voice.

'And I hope you all realise that drinking and driving is
extremely dangerous.' He was a relatively new teacher to the
school and had not been there last year when one of the senior
boys crashed his car into a tree after the Halloween disco in
the town hall. The rumour was it took over an hour to cut him

from the wreckage. Ruth remembered her Dad taking out his black tie from the handkerchief drawer, where it lay like a coiled up snake. When he came back from the funeral his umbrella was buckled from the wind.

'So what does my Dad give you for SH now?' asked Ruth.

'Oh, just the usual,' said Lisa. 'It's their job.' Ruth decided not to ask any more.

The kitchen clock said ten past nine.

'Hey Kate, remember bananas after ten,' said Lisa, clearing the cups away.

'What's bananas?' asked Ruth, like she already sensed it was a code word.

'Oh nothing you need to worry about,' said Kate in a not unkind way.

'It'll be time for your bed before that anyway.'

Ruth sighed with her shoulders and gave a weak smile.

Lisa filled her hot water bottle and Kate came upstairs to switch off the light.

'Can you leave the door open please?' said Ruth. A large rectangle of light from the hall fell on the blue carpet. Ruth heard Kate shut the door downstairs and she lay on her back and watched her fish mobile turning in the half light. After a moment she pulled her pillow from beneath her head and held it above her, an inch from her nose. She closed her eyes and softly let it brush her lips. She was concentrating hard and her eyes screwed up tighter. She didn't know what he looked like close up. She thought of his red Adidas football shirt and the way his mouth hung open when he walked off the pitch. Her lips began to tickle like pins and needles as they trailed the cotton of the pillow case. She let the full weight of the pillow cover her face, hugging it with both arms. A trickle of saliva sat at the corner of her mouth and she needed air. Suddenly she felt utterly ridiculous. She threw the pillow back on to the mattress and plumped it up the way her mum did. With the hot water bottle between her feet, Ruth curled up, waiting for sleep to come.

She woke up to the thump of music coming from downstairs. It sounded like Adam Ant. The volume rose and fell as the living room door was opened and closed. Above the music there were squeals of laughter. Ruth lifted her head off the pillow, angling her ears to hear more. A male voice was talking loudly. The clanking of bottles or glasses. She sniffed the air and thought she could smell cigarettes.

After a while the music stopped and the voices fell to a mumble. In tip toe movements Ruth climbed out of bed and knelt on the floor pressing one ear against the carpet. She felt a chill as the thin nylon of her nightie clung to her skin with static. The living room door opened again and she heard heavy footsteps on the stairs. She crept back under the duvet. The bathroom light clicked on. Ruth did not see who went in but from her bed she could see a slice of the bathroom towel rail where the door had not closed properly. From the hall she heard Lisa's whispered shout.

'Sshh, be quiet up there for God's sake.'

The person in the bathroom must have knocked something over. A clattering noise. Ruth worried that it might be her mother's Chanel perfume, the one she had helped her Dad choose last Christmas. A retching noise was followed by the unmistakable sound of someone vomiting, the watery splatter as the sick hit the toilet bowl. Ruth gave an involuntary shiver. She could feel her heart pulsing like a frog trying to escape from her chest. She looked at the alarm clock beside her bed. Its fluorescent green hands said ten to one. She thought of her mum and dad. They would be on their way home soon, her mum driving, her dad relaxed in the heat of the car, classical music playing.

Downstairs there was panic in Lisa's voice.

'Jesus, Kate, get him out of there.' Footsteps clambered up the stairs two at a time and dragged whoever was in the toilet downstairs. There was a big kefuffle as if a cow had accidentally found its way into their hall. It was followed by a fan of light moving across Ruth's bedroom curtains and the crunch of tyres on gravel. It was as if thinking of them had brought them home quicker.

'Bloody hell. That's them now. Quick Ricky out the back door.' The back door opened and slammed shut. Ruth imagined Ricky Grant stumbling down the muddy lane in the dark. The shock of the cold sea air ruffling through his shiny, black hair. The baby-sitters must have rushed back into the living room. Silence again and seconds later the sound of the keys in the front door. Ruth heard her mum's voice.

'Girls, Hi. Sorry we're a bit late. How did you get on? No bother with the kids, I hope?'

The toilet thought Ruth, the bloody toilet hasn't been flushed. The thought came to her in slow motion like a road safety film of a horrific crash. She leapt out of bed and ran to the bathroom. The lino was cold beneath her feet and the horribly familiar smell of sickness hit her. She lowered the toilet seat, holding it squeamishly between finger and thumb. With the palm of her other hand she pushed the flush handle down and heard the swishing of the water as she ran back to bed, pulling the cover up to her neck.

When she heard Dad come into the bedroom she closed her eyes, then tried to peek out through spidery eyelashes.

'I thought I heard you up,' whispered her Dad, leaning over. His breath smelt of whisky, half sour, half sweet.

'Did you have a good time with the baby-sitters?'

'Yes,' she whispered, then slightly louder, 'Yeah, it was a magic laugh.'

'Good night then, love. Hope you get back to sleep.' He patted her head and pulled the door, leaving only a thin wedge of light behind them.

Maureen Macnaughtan

STRATHCLYDE WOMAN

The specky bampot knew fine
Well ah wis rotten wi drugs.
They couldny get the pen workin.
Ah wisht ah hudny signed
That bloody Donor Card.
Ah'm jagged, he disny shut up.
'Better to do it now,
Think of all the people
Who will benefit by your action.'

Ah never lik'd that doactor,
Whit a torn-faced nyaff.
He wis right aboot the fags.
Mind, ah did cut doon
Ah'm gettin on good style
Nae freis, brekwist wis yoghurt,
Even went joggin tae work.
Mibby if ah'd lost merr weight –
Ye dinna get askin the enemy.

It wis hard oan ma Doogie.
Am'm sure he kent fine
Bit we played the gemme.
The wee soul wis awfy guid,
Ye should've seen him
He come tae the hospital
Wi hauf the shoap.
Sweeties, boatles a skoosh,
Even booked us up fur Spain.

He thought ah'd jump at it.
We we're gaun on hoaliday
Ah wis tae get new claes,
Ma Maw wid keep the weans.
Me'n him wid sit thegither
Lik when we wis winchin.
The staff wur pure brilliant
Me fur the off, an us
Lookin at aw the brochures.

Ma aul filla went quick,
Nae hingin aboot fur him.;
Booze, gamblin, Hell mend him
He wis such a swine.
Ma Mammy couldny get peace,
The big waster turned nasty
If there wis nae bevvy.
He'd gie her a showin up
Shoutin an bawlin the odds.

The neeburs we're sorry fur Maw
Some wid send roon messages.
She'd be knockin her pan in
Feedin us an workin aw day,
An that stinkin rotten pig
Wid start kickin the door.
Whit a life she hud, the
Poor soul wis demented wi him
Pittin the hammer oan her.

Ah met Doogie at the jiggin
He wis aye a bit shy,
Ah sorta bumpt inty him.
His Mammy took the petted lip.
The stuck-up-cow hud
Plans fur her only boay.
See when ah telt ma Maw
That the hale lot we're T.T.
She couldna stoap greetin.

Ah canna believe it,
Efter hunners an hunners o
Years, lyin in the grun,
Some Martian oot fur a
Dauner goes an thaws ma heid.
They've goat me wired up.
Ah'm that glad ma Doogie
Canna see the mess ah'm in.
The poor bugger wid be mental.

Funny, ah wis dreamin aboot Spain.
The heat oan ma doosh
Is at least a hunner watt,
Some clown keeps feedin the meter.
Ma eyes ur pure nippin
Wi the fumes aff this watter.
It's nae right tae huv folk
Floatin in a jeely jaur.
Well, ah'm tellin them Nothin.

Aonghas MacNeacail

AN DUIBHRE BEÒ

ged is fhada bho choinnich sinn, a dhuibhre
tha thu fhathast na do chat dhomh
drùidhteach, dubh agus diamhair
na do nathair, na do luibhe

cluinneam do chrònan seòlta
caora, mas fhìor
's mar a tha thu ag èaladh
troimh dhoras dùinte mo shùilean
do dhuilleach mar neòil gun shoillse
ga mo phasgadh, ga mo phasgadh
ann an cille thruagh mo thuairmsean fhìn
agus nuair a bha mi an dùil
gun robh mo mhacmeanmhain balbh
leig thusa mach mo bhòcain

THE LIVING DARK

though it's long since I first met you, darkness
you are still a cat to me
pervasive, dark and secret
you are snake, you are weed

I hear your cunning purr
pretend to be sheep
and the way you slither
through the closed door of my eyes
your foliage like clouds without light
wrapping me, wrapping me
in the meagre cell of my own surmise
then when I have assumed
that my imagination's dumb
you release my bogeymen

CHA DO THILL DUINE RIAMH

cha do thill duine riamh dha bheatha fhèin
le seonaidh shuas air trèigsinn is
seonag shìos nach gluais a chaoidh
is' aig an robh na sgeulachdan lid air lid'
esan a sheinneadh gach rann anns a' bhliadhna

coimhead a-nise na raointean a choisich e
èisd ri a guth ann an doras na bùtha

do chuimhne amhàin
do chuimhne amhàin
fhad's is beò thu

ged a bhiodh a'chraobh ud nas àirde
bha na fiùran anuiridh
nas àirde na druim àrd na cille
ged a bhiodh a' chraobh ud nas àirde
cò dhèanadh fèill
is an tè seo air sìneadh gu làr

WE DO NOT RETURN

we do not return to our own lives
with johnnie up now passed away
and jeannie down who'll never stir
she who had the stories word for word
he who could sing every verse in the year

look now at the country he walked in
listen for her voice in the door of the shop

your memory only
your memory only
as long as you live

though that tree should be taller
which was sapling last year
taller than the high ridge of the church
though that tree should be taller
who'd make a feast
when this tree reclines on the ground

AIR LATHA SGLEÒTHACH 'S TU BHUAM

mise nam shuidh' air oir linne
's na beanntan thall
a' luasgan fon cheò

tha dùnadh an fhoghair
na uallach orm, mar a tha e
slaodadh nan latha bhuam, air
sleamhain-rathad sìos dhan dubhair

agus an duilleag àlainn na
h-èideadh grìosaich, a' tuiteam
socharach mall na shlabhraidh
sheunta dha mo shùilean,

anns am faic mi
camhanaich do bhilean, oidhche dhìon
do ghruaig, tràth-nòin bàn do bhroillich,
's tu na d' shamhradh buan dhomh

A HAZY DAY, APART FROM YOU

I sit beside a firth,
see the peaks beyond
restless in the mist

enclosing autumn is
a weight on me, the way it
drags the days from me, on
its slide down into darkness

while the lovely leaf in its
dress of embers, falling
shyly, makes a slow mesmeric
chain that holds my eyes,

in which I see
dawn in your lips, safe night
in your hair, pale noon in your breast,
and you my enduring summer

Kevin MacNeil

BALBH

Bha mi ag iarraidh dàin is todaidhean
is sìth-inntinn a thoirt dhut.
Chunna mi thu an-diugh
's cha robh càil ri ràdh
ach anns a' bhad fhuair mi a-mach
cò ris a tha e coltach
gach uair a chì thu mapa
's chan fhaic d' inntinn càil
ach seo far an d'fhuair iad a bhàta.
Chan fhaic mise càil ach mi
fhìn a' snàmh gu mall
tro rùmannan uaine d' inntinn,
mo ghàirdeanan a' faireachdainn
nan tonn troma man sruth
de ghlacan briste.
Latha a bha seo, chùm thu deagh
ghrèim air mo làimhe man failm
neo-mhuinighineach.

DUMB

I wanted to bring you poems & toddies & peace of mind.
I saw you today and there was nothing at all to say but I
learned in an instant what it is like every time you see a map
& your mind sees nothing but this is where they found his
boat. I see myself swimming slowly through the green rooms
of your mind, my arms feeling the heavy waves like a stream
of broken embraces.
You who once gripped my hand like an unreliable rudder.

AN ACARSAID

na rionnagan a' deàrrsadh san uisge
na rionnagan a' deàrrsadh na mo chridhe
an Cuan Sgìth mar sgàthan dorch
's do phòg mu dheireadh
air mo ghruaidh fhathast
balbh, fuar, fad air falbh
mar seann ghealach
a' cuimhneachadh air acarsaid eile

THE HARBOUR

the stars shining in the water the stars
shining in my heart the Minch like a
dark mirror and your farewell kiss
still on my cheek – dumb, cold,
distant – like an old moon
remembering another harbour

Iain Mac a' Phearsain

SAIL

an e an dearbh sàil
a' laighe sèimh air mo bhilean
mar do chorragan fhèin

mar a laigh thu orm
ri taobh a' chuain
boinne am beul na gaoithe

a' sèideadh far mo choise
a' sileadh far mo ghlùine
mar a dhèanamaid ùrnaigh

cha do chreid mo shùilean
an sealladh a ghlac iad
a' tionndadh chun na mara

an dearbh chruth
a mheall mo bhuadhan
nuair bha mi a' cadal thall

cò chanas an fhìrinn
cò chuireas ceist air an fheasgar
cò ghabhas e

sàil air do chorragan
sàil air do bhilean
sàil air m'inntinn fhèin

John Scott MacPherson

SALT WATER

is it the same, salt-water
lying gentle on my lips
as your own fingers

as you lay upon me
beside the sea
a drop in the wind's mouth

blowing 'cross my legs
dripping down my knees
as we would pray

my eyes did not believe
the view they seized
turning to the sea

the same form
that deluded my wits
and I sleeping overseas

who will say the truth
who will question the evening
who will claim it

salt-water on your fingers
salt-water on your lips
salt-water on my mind

GUN URRAM

chan e fàidh a th'annam
ged a bhios mi ag aisling tuilleadh 's a' chòir
ach tha mi a' dol a sgur
mun tig an còrr
mar a bhios mi ag ràdh gach uair

agus thuirt thu fhèin
gun robh fios agad mar tha
gun tachradh seo
an seo a-nochd
leis an acras gar tolladh

chan ann a-mhàin na do dhùthaich fhèin
nach faigh thu urram a' bhàird
ach uaireanan
ann an leabaidh chumhang ùr
fada thall a' chuain

agus thuirt thu 's dòcha
gun cuireadh seo crìoch air a h-uile sian
ged a bha do shùillean a' dìteadh
na thuirt do bheul
's bha mise fuireach ris a' chòrr

WITHOUT RESPECT

I'm not a prophet
though I tend to dream too much
but I'm going to stop
before the rest come
as I claim every time

and you said
that you already knew
this would happen
but tonight
what with want boring through us

not only in your own land
do the bard's honours elude you
but sometimes
in a narrow new bed
across the seas

and you said – perhaps
this would put an end to everything
though your eyes sentenced
what your mouth proposed
and I waited for the rest...

LEUM NAM BUFFALO

bha an duine dearg ann
an t-àm a bha sin
nuair a bhuaileadh am buffalo na raointean
le fuaim na tàirneanaich

agus bhiodh daoine a' fuireach
fad a' gheamhraidh
gus an tàinig aiteamh na gaoithe
a' *chinook* a chuir sgleò orra
gus an do thuit na beathaichean bochd
far na creige àird
a bhiodh a' toirt dhaibh
sealladh na sìorraidheachd
mionaid no dhà mus do dh'eug iad:

a' phrèiridh mhòir na sìneadh
fichead mìle air falbh
cho farsainn ris a'chuan
's gun do theab iad smaointinn
gur ann ann an cuideachd Mhaois
a bha iad
a' sgaradh a' chuain
air an t-slighe gu tìr a'gheallaidh
Eipheit-Alberta

air am buaireadh leis an fhìrinn
a' falach ann an gath na grèine
a' priobadh a-mach
air latha grianach garbh geamhraidh

agus thogadh an duine dearg
suas a shùilean
gus deò a thoirt dhan Spiorad Mhòr
'son gaoth 's grian
sgòthan 's feur
an tìr air leth
agus àm bàis
ann an uillt staoin na fala
aig bonn na creige

HEAD-SMASHED-IN-BUFFALO-JUMP

the redman was there
at that time
when buffalo would beat the great plains
with thunder sounds

and people would wait
all winter
till the wind's thaw
the chinook that muddled them
till the poor beasts fell
from off the high cliff
giving them a vision of eternity
a moment or two before death

the great prairie stretched out
twenty miles away
as far as the sea
till they almost figured
they were in the company of Moses
separating seas
on the way to the promised land
Egypt – Alberta

overcome by the truth
hiding in a sun's ray
peeking out
on a wild sunny winter day

and the redman would raise his eyes
to grant lifespark to the Great Spirit
for wind and sun
clouds and tallgrass
the land alone
and death's time
in shallow rivulets of blood
at the bottom of the cliff

*Head-Smashed-In-Buffalo-Jump is a site in southern
Alberta; a cliff used by Indian buffalo hunters before
the arrival of the whiteman and the horse.*

Eve Lilith MacRae

LETTER FROM AN ISLAND IN THE MIDDLE OF AN UNKNOWN SEA

Robert,
Husband ay mine, ahm missin ye badly, for thair is a gapin hole in ma haert whair ye are not. Ah huv cried masel tae sleep these past three nights wi oot yir airms aroond me. It hus bin a rare long time since last we held each other, but since ahv arrived here ah huv fair noticed yir absence. An if ah fear that yir sleepin wi somewan else this night, as the sun sinks red intae the red ocean, it's coz ah still hope tae see ye again.

This is tae be ma fourth night on this island. Ah dinnae know how many other nights ah'll bide here. Ah keep waitin tae see some ship passin, but the oceans are aw empty, empty as ma haert.

Danu is deid. She died in ma airms as ah wis strokin her hair, her fine blond Irish hair. She just stopped breathin, an ah sensed her spirit leave. Ah saw it wi ma other eye. It wis gold an pink an shimmerin. Beautiful. An ah knew she wis off tae a better place. But it didnae stop the tears fae fallin fae ma eyes. An the salt ay thaim made me thirsty as a mariner, an ah dooned the last ay oor stale watter as a mournin ay her passin.

Robert, ah hud tae throw her overboard, cos ah knew that maybe eftir a few days mair ay hunger ahd huv hud tae eat at her. An ah couldnae huv bared the thought. Coz ah knew in ma haert that the urge for survival grows on some an diminishes on others wi the passin ay time. An ah knew ah wis a survivor, an that in the end ah would dae anythin tae survive, an it would be an abomination on ma soul tae eat the dead flesh ay a dear friend.

Oh Robert, when ah lugged her overboard ah didnae think straight. Ah thought she would sink doon an that'd be her, but she just floated thair, oot ay reach, but e'er so close. What wi the winds huvin died doon tae nowt, it wisnae till yon night that ah lost sight ay her. Ah fell asleep, knowin full well she wis bobbin aboot somewhair just oot thair. Ah fell asleep till well eftir the sun would huv risen, wi ma haert in bits. Ah woke wi the wind an rain lashin ma face an ah wis so pleased tae slake ma thirst that ah didnae think ay Danu wan time. An ah wis fair afeart an aw, for it wis a fragile craft ah wis in an it felt like it wis made ay matchsticks an rabbit glue on that heavin ocean.

Ah wis sure ah wis for the sharks or whatever dreadful beasts that live under the skin ay the ocean.

Well Robert, the light is failin awfy fast the now, so different fae back hame. Ah'll huv tae wait till the mornin light before ah can write ye any mair.

Husband ay mine, Robert ma love, it is not the mornin eftir, nor the wan eftir that, nor am ah sure how many it is eftir. When ah awoke, that ah can remember, ah wis bathed in a dreadful slimy sweat an ma boadice an skirts were soaked in horrible skitters, the thinness ay pish, an ah wis so cramped up wi the pain ay it aw ah wis sure ah wis goin tae die. It wis terrible. The fevers were ragin on me an ah wis seein demons an faeries an all sorts, an ah wis prayin tae the Lord like ah nivir did in all the times ah wis drummed up tae the kirk wi ma mammy an daddy an aw ma sisters an brithers. Ye would laugh at me, wi yir heid full ay aw that modern thinkin, but ah think maybe the Lord did get me through it, an in ma haert ah think it is providence an wan day ah will see ye again.

Ah think aboot Australia an wonder what it is like, an ay how yir earnin five times what ye were earnin in Glesga, an ahm so proud ay ye bein an engineer on the railroads. Ah often imagine ye howfin they big sleepers wi yir big airms. An how ah wish yir big airms were roond me now, ma darlin. Ye say it's hot in Australia. It's hot here tae, awfy hot. Thair are many strange things on this island, an sometimes ahm very afeart, but ah know wi ma other eye ahm tae see ye again. Ah know it with ma haert tae. Ah love ye, Robert MacRae.

Ah huv nivir felt a heat like this. It is tae hot tae wear claes. But ah huv made a coverin fae the linin ay ma skirts, an while it is thin an cool, it is baith modest an becomin. An besides ma airms are burnt raw red wi the sun, worse than the hottest days ay summer when we've bin a roondin an shearin the sheep or cuttin doon the grain. Ahm sittin under the shade ay a tall tree wi the hugest, fattest leave ye huv e'er seen an nae branches or nowt, just a long lean stem.

For a while eftir ma fever broke, when ma heid wis no quite fair, ah wis dancin like a gull, nakid as the day ah wis born, along the edge ay the beach, wi aw ma shitey skirts washed oot an leein oot in the sand tae dry, an ah felt a strange kind ay happiness come doon on me, the like ahv nivir felt before. Only the next day wis ma heid screwed on right again, an ah hud tae taste the shame for ma wanton ways. But it is ay hot here, ma dearie dear, an a wonder if it's such a sin, wi no fowk tae see.

It is no a big island, aboot forty or fifty acres only, an thair is naebody else camped here, but strange birds an small dragon-like beasts that bathe on the rocks by the heat ay the day. They are but two foot long an should prove nae danger. The island is thick wi aw sorts ay trees an thair are fruits an nuts ay many strange types in plenty. But ah miss ma meat an feel a strong hunger for it. Though ah couldnae find it in ma haert tae devise ways ay killin these weird brightly coloured birds that caw an yammir, each tae its fashin.

An ah think wi shame now that the day eftir the storm ah wis cryin ma stupidity at throwin oot Danu's puir wee boady ontae they watters, what wi the hunger gnawin at ma belly worse than hellfire an the sweat pourin oot ma hair roots an blindin ma eyes. Ah tell ye Robert, ah would huv eaten at Danu's pale flesh wi oot thinkin that day. An ah gie thanks tae God that He found me this island the very next morn, cos ah swear ah would huv died. That night Robert, ah wis sair afeart. Ah couldnae sleep for the pains in ma belly an ah wis mortally minded ay oor child hae ah lost on the third day ay the sailing. Ye nivir knew that ah wis carryin, but ah knew the night yir seed touched mine, ah just knew, an ah wis sair grievin for losin it, sair grievin an sair tae the pit ay ma stomack, like a hunger ah nivir knew until ah knew hunger for real. What a night. Ah dinnae remember sleepin, but ah must huv, for the next thing ah knew, the wee boatie wis stranded on a sand spar, but twenty yards fae this island, an the sun wis blazin intae ma eyes so fierce ah thought it wis the light ay the Lord. An for a wee second thair, Robert, ah thought ah wis deid an hud come tae paradise, but then ah felt the cramps in ma neck an shoodirs an ah knew ah wis still of this mortal coil. For thair will be no boadily pains in the world here eftir. That ah know.

Oh Robert, ahm sair grieved for Danu's passin an sair griev-ed for yir brither. Ye must tell Sandy that her passin wis painless an that her soul now resides in heaven. She wis a puir soul, afflicted by weakness ay the bones an the rickets, but she hud a strong will tae survive, like me. An even though ah knew she wouldnae, wi ma other aye, ma haert did but hope. Robert, thair were seven ay us in that wee craft an only ah, by the grace ay God's love, did survive. An ah cannae help but wonder why ah wis so graced. Does the Lord huv a purpose for me?

Ah huvnae written now for several days, Robert ma love, for ma haert hus bin full ay sorrow an anger, an ah couldnae write ye wi that burden on me. Even now, ah cannae bring the light intae ma haert. But ahm filled tae burstin wi love for ye an cannae lee ma pen dry any longer.

The news ay oor ship's doonin must huv reached ye an Sandy by now an ah know ye must be heavy hearted at the death ay me an Danu, an ye willnae, bein the men that ye are, bide wi false hopes ay oor survival.

Ah huv bin watchin for ships, an the day before did see wan, far on the horizon, but it didnae come anywhair near tae this wee island, an ma haert sunk tae ma knees for seeing it so, an ah wondert if ma angels were feedin ma ears wi ungodly lies, tae lift up ma hopes an dash thaim cruelly against the rocks. But ah hear thaim an they are talkin soft in ma ears, liftin away ma fears as ah sit here wi ma ankles in the warm foam ay this huge sea, an ah know in ma haert that it willnae be long before a ship takes me tae Australia an joins me tae ye once again.

Ah huv aw yir buiks, but wan. Ahv lost 'The Rights Of Man', but yir Ruskin an Dickens an aw the others are safe in ma bag. Ahv torn the blank pages fae thaim, an ah know ye'll be sair aboot that, but thair wis nowt aw else tae write on. Ah huv leafed through they buiks an can only make a wee bit sense ay thaim, for they are writ in the sassenach tongue an ah hud but few years ay sculin an hated the dominie's ways for aw that, wishin only tae be daein the milkin or collectin the chookie's eggs. But ahv bin thinkin ay ye readin they buiks by the haerth, eftir yir twelve hoors at the shipyairds, an thinkin so, ma haert hus bin filled wi wrath for the injustice ay it aw. When ah think ay they wee nancy malkies wi thair heids in the clouds up Kelvingrove, just a mile away fae Pertick, wi ye sweatin away at the shipyaird an wi ten times the sensibility ay they wee twats. Thair, ahv said it now. Shame on ma cursin mouth. But when ah think ay the injustice ay it aw it gets me right in the gut an ah want tae lash oot an smack they wee nancy malkies wi the back ay ma haun, wi thair plummy voices an safty boadies which huvnae done a day's labour in thair lives. Honest tae God Robert, ah could curse till the cock crows for it aw. Ah wish we'd nivir gone doon tae Glesga. Its dirt hus got intae ma soul, an even on this island, hunderts ay miles fae it, ah feel its poison on me. We would huv bin happy if we'd steyed on the ferm, puir but happy, if yon bastarn factotum hudnae pit us oot on oor erses.

Is Australia really the paradise ye say it is? Is thair nae puir, nae starvin, naebody pit oot ay thair hames? It's hard tae imagine, an empty paradise just waitin for the findin. An ye say it's a hundert times and mair the size ay Scoatland. Ah cannae tell ye how hard that is tae picture. Ah mind oor trip fae Inversnoddy tae Glesga. Three days walk it wis tae Inverness, an a full day's ride on the train fae thair tae Glesga. How long must it take tae cross Australia? An ye say that the middle part ay it is just burning stane, an that thair's nae watter tae be hud, an that many huv died thair prospectin for gold.

Ah wish ye hud writ mair Robert, ma mind is fair taken wi this strange land that is tae be ma new hame. Ah huv yir letters here, baith ay thaim, but the ink hus ran wi the salt watter. But ah know what ye say in thaim by haert. Ah think aboot Australia wi its haert ay fire an skin ay velvet an wonder if aw is really guid thair. Tell me it's so Robert. Tell me it's better than oor wee ferm in Inversnoddy.

Yesterday, Robert, wan ay they red an blue birds wis walkin along the edge ay the clearin an ah spoatit it wis carryin its wing an ah knew it wisnae a far cry fae death, so a clobbered its wee heid wi a muckle big bit wid an ah roastit it guid at the fire. It tuik me many long hoors tae get the fire goin, but ah got it usin stane as flint an wee bits ay dried grass an now it's blazin away guid style. The meat on the bird wis better than anythin ah e'er tasted fae a chookie, an ahm determint ah'll huv another before the night is oot. Wondrous as they are tae behold, thair are hunderts ay thaim an ahm fair ravenous for meat.

Ahv collected enough wid tae keep this fire goin for a couple ay days. Ah know thair's another ship near an ma smoke will draw it nearer still. Ma angels huv shown me.

Ahm goin tae pit this note in the boatil an set it off tae sea. Ah know fine it willnae get tae ye, but ah hud tae write it for ye, hud tae write it, for ma soul wis achin wi the pain ay it. Ma ship is comin an soon we will be thegithir, an ay aw this ah will tell ye nowt. For how can a wife unburden her haert? A woman's haert is nae empty vessel, but it is capable ay haudin mair grief than any life can gie it. Ah love ye Robert MacRae, yir a guid man, but ye cannae carry ma burden for me.

Wi love an fond kisses,
Lily.

John Maley

RORY'S KITCHEN DRAWER

The kitchen drawer in Rory's flat was crammed with papers and objects, old bills, instruction leaflets, guarantees, receipts, jumbled up with buttons, pens, sellotape, tacks, there were even a few johnny bags (unused) amongst the mess. Don stood in front of the open drawer like a mesmerised child.

'Fart in a trance.'

Don turned to look at Terry, who was carefully packing books into cardboard boxes.

'We'll be here forever if you just stand there like a fart in a trance.'

Terry was such a fussy queen, but his organising skills were appreciated by Rory. When Rory had asked Terry to take care of things when he died, he had agreed immediately. Don was glad he hadn't been put on the spot. He knew that some people coped with grief by burying themselves in practicalities. He had watched his sister scrub their parents' house like a demented Stepford Wife for two days after their mother died. Terry was like that, his manner at the funeral had been so officious it had pissed everybody off. Don had always been a broody kind of guy. Opening the drawer in Rory's lovely, bright, sunflower yellow kitchen to see the little bits and pieces that bulged and dragged in a rough mass as he gave the drawer a final yank, it was just so sad. It was the very impersonality of it. He and Terry had already packed a box full of letters and photos, some they would destroy and some they would keep. That had been tragic, but strangely comforting. The anonymous flotsam and jetsam in the kitchen drawer was something else. The guarantees. There was one for a vacuum cleaner, an iron, a toaster, a portable TV.

'Check this, Don.'

Terry held up a slim paperback.

'Giovanni's Room. James Baldwin. This was a wee present from me.'

He read from the flyleaf.

'To Rory. Lots of love and a happy thirtieth. May 1990. Terry. Kiss Kiss.'

Don was silent. Terry sat hunched over one of the boxes with the Baldwin in his hand. For a moment, Don thought he was crying. But then he saw Terry place the book carefully into a box and go onto the next shelf, steady and purposeful. He was one particular poof. Don hated shopping with Terry because he was so particular about things. If he liked a shirt or a jacket or even a pair of underpants he couldn't just grab it, take it to the counter and crash the cash for it. He had to rummage around until he found out exactly what it was made of, the washing instructions, he would even tug slyly at the seams to check the stitching. Once he had emerged from under a rail of shirts in Gap and declared emphatically 'I'd never wash that at forty degrees!'

Of course he had to try everything on. Don had hovered in countless shops whilst Terry had preened himself in the changing rooms, much to the chagrin of store security guards. One had even joked about setting the fire alarm off to get him out of a changing room. Terry was unrepentant.

'I know I'm a fussy cow, but I've yet to regret a purchase.'

Don put both hands in the drawer and rummaged around in an effort to appease Terry. He began to drop the obvious rubbish into a plastic carrier bag at his feet. He knew he should simply turn the drawer upside down into the bag and go back to the lounge to help Terry. He was stalling. It had all happened so fast.

Terry had got a call from Rory to say that he was ill and as Terry had commented cryptically, 'wasn't going to get any better'. Rory seemed to go down pretty quickly. Terry had naturally become his confidante and executor. Don had imagined Terry stationed constantly at Rory's sickbed, wearing a big black cloak and scribbling away with an old feather-quill pen. But it was what was needed, someone to defuse the emotional time-bomb (that was ticking louder each passing day) with an increasingly tedious list of Practical Things That Needed To Be Done. Once, when Terry was discussing the need to put Rory's house on the market, Don had seen a solitary tear trickle down Terry's face. Terry had quickly brushed the tear away and said, 'Tasks now, tears later.'

Don had always fancied Rory. He had never particularly liked the man, too posh and pompous. But he was so effortlessly handsome. It was the lack of effort that rankled. It had been Rory's genetic destiny to be gorgeous. He played on it. Don had never fancied Terry. But Terry had been a loyal friend to Don. A pain in the arse, but loyal. You needed him, he was there. He didn't always say the right thing, he didn't always do the right thing, but he was there and he was on your side. Loyalty, felt Don, was a rare treasure he had seldom found with friends or lovers. Things changed too much, that was it. Friends became acquaintances became strangers. Lovers left, interminably they left. After one night or one year, they left. There was nothing wrong with changes, Don welcomed changes, but it was all so fucking transient. He looked down at the kitchen drawer and thought of Rory reduced to ashes and his flat like a shipwreck yielding up its contents.

'Finished!'

Terry stood with his hands on his hips and cocked his head, peering into the kitchen. Don emptied the drawer into the plastic bag.

'Me too.'

They drove home with the books and CDs and bric-a-brac they had retrieved from the flat. Terry was still intent on speaking strictly business.

'I'll go over tomorrow and gut the place. Bit of elbow grease. There's a couple coming to view it next Monday.'

Don was quiet.

That night Terry and Don went to Delilah's. They used to go there with Rory. There had been some kind of connection, some kind of inexplicable bond between Terry and Rory. Don tried to think what it was as he sat in a booth with Terry. There was a kind of emotional coldness about them. Coldness. That was too strong a word, too judgmental. They just didn't give much away. Terry had once confided in Don that a man had broken his heart when he was twenty and he'd never really got over it. Without trust, he said, you can't love.

Don checked out the crowd in Delilah's. It was Friday night. It was a young crowd. Skinny young guys who seemed ten times more confident than he'd ever been at their age. Or maybe he was just tired. He was tired of Terry. His caution, his brisk, no-nonsense, businesslike approach. Life's not tidy, Don wanted to tell him. It's a mess.

'When did we last laugh?'

Terry eyed him suspiciously and took a frugal sip of his rum and coke.

'My oldest pal just died. I don't get the joke.'

Don worked on his pint of lager. Terry drummed his fingers on the table and stared wistfully out of the window. It began to rain and the street outside shone blue. Across the road they could see the posters on the derelict building flap and peel.

From where Don sat he could clock Bob the Bouncer at the front door, through the glass of the interior door. Don fancied Bob. He was sexy in a caveman kind of way. He was a good-looking guy and the fact he was straight made him irresistible. Don wasn't so sure Bob was totally straight. He had once over-heard Bob say to another bouncer friend something about it didn't matter man or woman as long as it had a hole.

'You're staring at that Bob again! He'll lamp you one.'

'He can get me in a half-nelson anytime.'

'You'd run a mile.'

Don looked at Terry. He looked tired and sexless and lost. Terry had said he was celibate. He had had enough of it all. Don thought maybe he had just got tired of looking. Don hadn't had it in six months. He hadn't honestly missed it that much. His last encounter had been pretty disastrous. A drunken young queen who had puked on his bathroom floor and snored like a giant. When he thought now of Rory, a beautiful big bear of a man who had withered and died so young, he didn't feel so horny.

'I'm going to powder my nose.'

Don watched Terry weave elegantly through the raucous customers who crowded the main drag, and upstairs to the loo. He took the opportunity to eye up the talent away from Terry's punitive gaze. The younger set had been joined by some smart-suited office-types, who looked like shop-window dummies. A biker with hair down to his feeble excuse for an arse drank a whisky in one go and fled. Maybe he was in the wrong place. Maybe they all were. Joanie danced behind the bar, wearing a huge copper-coloured wig and chandeliers for earrings. Don remembered seeing Rory in here. It was here in Delilah's where he had first set eyes on Rory. He had said to Terry, Adonis Alert. That was what he'd always say if he spied a handsome man.

'That's my pal, Terry had snapped, and snorted indignant-ly. Don had only recently started hanging around with Terry and harboured a forlorn hope that he'd get a boyfriend out of Terry's social circle. He had thought Rory had potential, but from their first conversation it was clear that there was only one man in Rory's life – Rory. Emptying Rory's kitchen drawer into a rubbish bag was as intimate as they had got. And that, decided Don, was curiously intimate.'

Terry came back eventually from the loo and sat brave and red-eyed in front of Don.

'That toilet's a bloody scandal. The dryer's broken, there's no paper towels, there's a bull dyke sniffing glue in one cubicle and a wank-off party in the other.'

Don leaned forward and brushed Terry's hair lightly with his fingers.

'You've been cryin'.'

Brian McCabe

THE HOST

'So. How. Was. The. Film.'

I was speaking in words but I didn't know what I was saying and my voice sounded thick and moronic and my mouth
was dry and my heart was hammering and my skin felt like a
cold chamois leather as I touched my face with my fingers – no
doubt the way I would normally touch my face with my fingers
if I was asking somebody about a film they'd been to see but
nothing was normal because here in my room was a man with
two heads.

For a horrible moment there was no response from anyone.
Had the words come out of my mouth at all or had they come
out sounding so strange that no one could make sense of them?
Was it my drugs? Had I forgotten to take my drugs? No, I had
taken them earlier. Had I got the dosage wrong? No, I distinctly
remembered taking the correct dosage.

'Well, I thought it was not a bad film, but the book –'

I felt a surge of gratitude to Jim. He had heard my question
and he was answering it. He was talking about the film, thank
God, so for the moment the attention of the room was not
focused on me. Had nobody noticed that I was trembling and
sweating and finding it difficult to speak?

I tried to pick up my glass and get it to my mouth. I
couldn't help turning a little to check that the man who had
been introduced to me as Douglas really did have two heads. I
had seen the other head quite clearly when he'd come into the
room and shaken my hand – lolling on his shoulder, as if It
couldn't quite support itself. I'd had to look away as I'd said
my pleased-to-meet-you.

It was there all right, I hadn't imagined it. In the dim light
of my room it was difficult to see the crumpled features of the
face, which was as pale as a cauliflower, yet I could make out
two screwed-up eyes, closed tightly under wispy, whitish eyebrows. I could see no clearly defined nose, but the lips were
unmistakable – they looked dry and cracked and unnaturally
old. Unnaturally old – that is the meaningless phrase that came
into my mind. The face had set into an expression which was
both sour and aloof. The way the lips curled down at one side
and up at the other made me think of a kind of bitter relish, as

if the owner of the mouth might take pleasure in sarcasm. At the same time there was something dreadfully vulnerable in the face's frozen sneer and the way the head lolled against the back of the armchair Douglas was sitting in – to all appearances a dead appendage. And no one seemed to have noticed it. Douglas himself appeared to be completely relaxed, as if utterly unaware of his encumbrance. He struck me as a congenial sort of person, probably in his early thirties. Apart from his other head, his appearance was quite ordinary. He had longish brown hair and a neat beard. He looked mildly interested in the world and had a constant, rather vacant smile. He wore a dark blue jacket, jeans and a casual, checked shirt.

But he had another head.

A red-haired woman I didn't know and whose name I hadn't taken in was disagreeing with Jim about the film and there were one or two comments interjected by the others – including Douglas. He didn't say much, and he was quietly spoken, maybe even a bit shy, but it was the kind of shyness which hints at an inner confidence.

They were having this good-natured, not-too-serious sort of debate about the merits of the film they'd been to see – for all the world as if nothing was out of the ordinary. I felt a moment of relief. The hammering of my heart was slowing down to a steady, heavy pounding. Although I'd raised my glass of wine to my lips I still hadn't taken a drink. Now I gulped some of it down in the hope that it would steady my nerves.

Was I over-reacting? I was with friends, after all. Jim was a friend, a good friend, I had known him since schooldays. He often went shopping for me, and that meant a lot to me. One or two of the others had been coming to see me for over a year now. There were strangers, but Jim often brought people back after a late-night film. It was supposed to do me good, help me cope with my agoraphobia, which he thought he understood. At least he understood that it wasn't just the fear of open spaces. He knew that it went hand-in-hand with claustrophobia. He understood that my fear was the fear of people. So he brought them round. It was supposed to encourage me to overcome it – or so I'd thought. Tonight he'd gone over the score. There were too many of them tonight. I couldn't see them clearly one by one as people, they were blurred into the same animal. I kept seeing movements of the feet and the hands but I didn't know whose they were. But although I saw them as one, at the same time I felt desperately outnumbered. It was difficult to hold on to my self.

Had Jim brought all these people round out of a spirit of charity or therapy? Maybe it was also convenient for him. Maybe he didn't want to take them all to his place. Here he was, acting for all the world as if he was doing me a favour by crowding out my house with the entire membership, I shouldn't wonder, of the local film club – one of whom had an extra head.

I glared at Jim, hoping to convey my displeasure with him in no uncertain terms, but he went on elaborating on some crucial discrepancy between the book and the film. He'd never brought this Douglas back before, I was certain of that, but people in the company seemed to know him, or if they didn't, they seemed to have accepted the fact that he had two heads with no trouble at all. Or maybe they were being polite. Maybe everyone in the room was doing his best not to look at it or talk about it, but inside they were panicking just as much as me. Or could it be that they were being quietly supportive? After all, an extra head, one which seemed to serve no purpose, must be a dreadful disability and Douglas seemed to be coping with it incredibly well. Maybe later on, I thought – but only if Douglas brings the subject up and wants to talk about it – maybe then I'll ask him if he has ever thought about the possibility of having it surgically removed. Oh God – no! I couldn't possibly ask him that – what was I thinking of?

Douglas leaned forward to flick his ash into the ash-tray on the coffee table. The head sprang forward to hang over his shoulder. With a start that set my pulse racing and almost made me yelp with fright, I noticed that one eye had opened a little and seemed to be peering at me as if from a great distance. When Douglas leaned back slowly – apparently he was listening to the post-mortem of the film with interest – the other head still hung forward, leaning one cheek on the collar of his jacket. I shuddered as I made out for the first time the tiny, creased nostrils. The head had, I was sure of it, taken a breath.

'So what do you think?'

Jim had turned to put this question to me and everyone now looked to me, their host, for an opinion.

'Well... I mean obviously... not having seen it –'

'But would you go to see it, on the basis of what we've said, or have we put you off going?'

'Well, I couldn't want to go to a cinema, but –'

What was I doing? Trying to make light of my own condition? Or drawing attention to it, to spare Douglas the attention of the room? But then, no one was looking at him, everyone was looking at me, and I didn't know how to go on.

Jim smiled and said:

'Yet you asked us what we thought of the film.'

'No, you don't know what... I wasn't asking you what the film was *about*, what I *meant* was... how much was it to get in, what was it like to sit in a place in the dark with... a crowd of other... I mean...'

I trailed off, trying to use the glass and the wine as an excuse to interrupt myself. I truly could not go on, not only because I was talking nonsense but also because the image of a crowded, darkened cinema had come into my mind, with its rows of silhouetted heads. One or two people laughed, apparently under the impression that I was being deliberately obtuse out of a sense of mischief. Jim looked at me in a pointedly puzzled way. I spluttered on my wine. I made the most of it, pretending that it had gone down the wrong way and I was having a coughing fit. Someone sitting next to me obliged by thumping me on the back, but in the middle of it I began to wheeze with disbelief. The head had now opened both eyes and was looking around the room.

Douglas took the cigarette from his mouth and, without even looking at what he was doing, placed it carefully in the other head's mouth. The other head sucked on it with some difficulty, then Douglas removed the cigarette and went on smoking it himself. A thin jet of smoke came from the other head's mouth, which was as desiccated as a shelled walnut, then it gave a little cough. How can I explain how this little cough made me feel? It was like a baby's cough, alarming because it hints at an articulacy and a history no one would expect of it. The sound of it made me shudder inside, as if on the verge of tears. I had to suppress a heavy sob welling in my chest. But now it was doing something else: I watched the head's mouth in awe as its dark, liverish tongue licked its cracked lips before speaking.

'That was very interesting.'

The eyelids of both eyes had parted, but were still stuck together at the corners in a way that looked extremely uncomfortable. The eyes, deep blue in colour, looked enormous in the shrunken face. But it was the look in the eyes... How can I describe it? There was infinite depth and distance in it, as if it was still looking at something in another world it had just come from. Yes, that was it, the head was waking up. The eye-lids blinked rapidly to unstick themselves completely and now the dark eyes looked directly at me.

'I don't mean what you were saying, but the way you were pretending to cough. Most people don't cough unless they have to, do they?'

The voice was rather thin and chesty, with a squeaky qual-ity that made it sound slightly comical. It was like the voice of a very old man, yet at times it also sounded like the voice of a child, made harsh by some bronchial illness. The other head smiled with one corner of its mouth, then uttered another babyish cough.

I couldn't answer. I was aware of the babble of voices around us. Apparently Jim was being witty and people were laughing. No one was paying the slightest attention to me or the head which had just addressed me. They were having a good time, apparently, but I was breathing hard and trembling and my hands were sweating so much they felt gloved in oil as I tried to find something to say to this head, this other head growing out of a man's neck.

I looked to Jim to rescue me, but now he was engrossed in some kind of intellectual duel with the red-haired woman. Of course, it was transparent to me that they were flirting. If only that had been all that was going on in my room – but no, there had to be a man with another head that wanted to talk to me. Douglas himself showed no interest whatsoever in the head even though it had woken up so conspicuously. He seemed completely preoccupied with stubbing his cigarette out, refill-ing his glass and following the conversation.

The crumpled face was waiting with an infinitely patient sadness for my response. I had to say something:

'I'm sorry. It's just that I... don't know how... I've never met a person with...'

'Two heads? Is that what you're driving at?'

'Well... I suppose so.'

The head, hanging at an angle so that it seemed to be peer-ing around a corner, did its best to nod with resignation.

'It's more common than you think.'

'What is?'
'Two heads.'
'Really? I had no idea.'
'Lots of people have two heads. Ask him.'

The other head indicated Douglas with a movement of its eyes and gave out a sharp little giggle. I glimpsed a row of neat, square teeth. Douglas raised the wine glass to his other head's lips, taking care not to spill it. This he managed to do without so much as glancing at the other head. Even so a drop of wine dribbled from the corner of the mouth. Douglas put the glass back down and took a tissue from his jacket pocket, with which he dabbed the other head's chin – though there was little in the way of what would normally be called a chin. All this he performed while staring straight ahead, apparently quite engrossed in the discussion about the film.

For a moment I saw Douglas and his other head as a music-hall double-act – the ventriloquist and his dummy. As if by telepathy, the other head looked at me and said:

'A gottle a geer.'

It chuckled at its own joke and the sound of its gargling laughter made me want to cry again. I had to fight back the shuddering sobs which wracked me inside and threatened to burst out at any moment. I call the other head 'it' because that is how I thought of this extraordinary phenomenon, but now I was forced to confront the fact that 'it' was a thinking, feeling being – 'it' was, I had to admit, a person. Had the poor man been someone's other head all his life? It was an intolerable thought.

The small, puckered face smiled up at me.

'How old do you think I am?'

My attempt at congenial laughter, as if we were engaged in the everyday social game of guess-how-old-I-am, left a lot to be desired. The small face with its vast, deep eyes watched me steadily as I brayed unconvincingly, waiting for my answer.

It was very difficult to tell how old he was. The eyes were as steady and watchful as a child's, yet they had a terribly knowing quality, as if they had seen the worst atrocities of humanity – the kind of thing most of us only read about in the newspapers. I could no longer meet their consuming gaze, and I studied Douglas – his main head and face, I mean, but also his clothes and his hands – before venturing:

'Well... younger than me – thirty? Thirty-one?'

The other head snorted briefly and said:

'That's his age. What about mine?'

'I have no idea when you... came about.'

'Came about? Oh, you make the mistake of thinking I grew out of *him*. No, my friend, you have it all wrong...'

I was alarmed by the way one of Douglas's hands suddenly stabbed a finger emphatically at his own chest.

'You see, *he* grew out of *me*.'

The hand now flew up to the uppermost side of the other head's face and scratched a loose flap of skin – it must be, I realised, an ear-lobe — then it swooped to the coffee-table and, in one fluid movement, lifted Douglas's glass of wine to the other head's mouth.

'My God, *you* did that!'

The other head drained the glass, set it down carefully on the coffee-table and smirked at me with pride, as if it had proved its point beyond question.

'My God. I see.'

The head nodded to me then, and with a look of profound sadness, said softly:

'*Now* you see.'

And I did see. I saw Douglas in a completely new way, now that it was clear that his other head could control his body. His main head, his normal head – or the one I had taken to be 'main' and 'normal' – now looked gross, a bland and doltish growth which had brutally unsurped the other head's place, pushing it aside and, for all I knew, drawing succour from it – like a fungus sapping the life of the tree from which it has swollen. His open, rather vacantly smiling expression now appeared to me as abhorrent as the sated leer of a callous parasite. The other head looked weak, drained of life, dying.

'Yes, he's taken over. I'm on the way out.'

'That's terrible!'

The other head smiled at me sadly.

'Oh, not so terrible. He's better looking than me. He's nicer, he'll get on all right. Less intelligent of course, and less honest – but that will be to his advantage. It was nice to meet you. You've been a very good host. But you look pale – you should get out more often.'

The other head yawned, winked at me, then the fragile eye-lids drooped and closed. He snuffled a little before his breathing slowed to a barely perceptible whisper in the air.

Douglas leaned back and the head swung behind his neck and subsided among the shadows of the armchair. His dominant head turned to look at me, as if he expected me to speak. Everyone was looking at me, waiting for me to speak. Jim had asked me a question and now he was repeating it:

'Are you all right?'

I tried to pick up my glass, but my hand shook uncontrollably. Thankfully the glass was almost empty. Someone relieved me of it, there were other people's hands and faces everywhere, then Jim said something about there being too many for me.

'One too many, just one too many.'

I looked at Douglas meaningfully as I said it and his eyes widened with baffled alarm. He stood up, and there was a sudden consensus in the room: everyone was standing up, draining glasses, putting coats and scarves on. The blur of all that activity made me feel nauseous, dizzy. Voices kept offering me their apologetic thanks.

Jim, crouching down beside my chair, asked me again if I was all right. This really was the last straw. He brings enough people to my house to fill a small cinema – one of them a double-header into the bargain – then he asks me if I'm all right!

I stood up, pushing him aside and shouted:

'*I'm* all right. Ask your friend there how his other head is. Ask him if *he's* all right!'

But Douglas was shuffling hurriedly into the hallway, where a few of the others were already waiting to leave. Jim looked at me with puzzled concern.

'Take it easy now. We're going, okay?'

'About time too.'

Jim turned and raised his eyebrows to the woman with red hair. It was evident to me that they had formed an unspoken pact. It would be back to his place, or hers, for sexual congress. But would it bring them closer to each other, or even to themselves? Somehow I did not think so. Jim said he'd call round in a day or two, thanked me for my hospitality and said they'd see themselves out. That was just as well, because I didn't feel particularly like standing around in my own doorway, exposed to the elements as I exchanged farewells with him and his army of film buffs. Let them go out into the street, under the empty sky. It was all right for them, they could do that with their eyes wide open and their heads held high, without the dread and the panic and the keeping near the wall and the scurrying for cover like a beetle when its stone is overturned.

When the front door eventually closed, I breathed more freely. The room seemed to settle into place around me, it became familiar again, but I felt exhausted by the evening's events. I wanted the warm cocoon of my bed. In reality it would be cold, unless I filled myself a hot water bottle, and I felt too tired to do that. It was all I could do to tidy up the glasses and bottles and ash-trays before going to the bathroom to clean my teeth.

As I pulled the switch-cord, the sudden bright light made my reflection jump out of the mirror at me. The roar of the Xpelair couldn't drown out my gasp of outrage at what I saw. It was there, no matter how often I wiped the condensation from the mirror with my sleeve, a mushroom-like swelling on my neck: the face was not fully formed, but already I could make out the mildly interested eyes and the constant, rather vacant smile.

J. Derrick McClure

A DISAPPINTIT WOOER

Frae Mireille *o* Frédéric Mistral, Cant Quatren,
stanzas 4–6 an 18–28.
Owerset frae the Provençal by J. Derrick McClure.

Allan the hird cam first tae woo.
In Allan's toun, nae want o ou!
A thousan maillies moups the winter girse
Alang Loch Finnart's growthy braes:
An syne, fan comes the linthenin days
An corn's in aicher green, he gaes
An caas tae Grampian sheilins aa his hirse.

I hear forbye, an aiblins richt,
Nine shearin-fowk, or Beltane nicht
Hes vrocht three days for Allan – men weel-kent!
Aye, an the cheil fa beirs awa
The wechty fleeshes fite, an aa:
The wee hird tee, a word maun faa
Fa taks the fowk their bickers, blythelie bent!

But fan the simmer days is by,
An on the Hielan muntains ley
The snaa atour the bothies gins tae sweel,
Doun tae the braid an gowstie Carse
Tae had them fat on winter girse
Frae Grampian glens an ballochs – sirse,
Ye bede tae see yon michty hirsel speil! ...

He'd quat his yowes wi jist ae plan:
Tae speir for bonnie Mirren's hann.
But stuid forenenst her, habberin a wee,
He said jist: 'Can ye shaa, my quine,
A gait or pad, nae eith tae tyne,
Wull lead me tae the Hielan line?
Iddergates, lass, I dout I'll ne'er win free!'

The lannart lassie wesna blate,
An said: 'Jist tak the furrit gait!
An seen ye'll finn Glen Fassach's hirstie mosses.
Folla the winnlin sloch ennlang,
A muckle cairn ye'll see or lang;
An syne ye'll goam, as on ye gang,
Twa staunin steens wi unco kerven crosses.

'Yon's fit they caa the Giant's Slap.'
'Thank ye, my hinnie,' said the knap.
'A thousan yowes – my kenmerk's on them aa –
Maun quat the Carse the morn wi speed
An sclim the bens: I'm gyaan aheid
Tae merk faar best tae faal an feed,
An faar's the eithest rodd the flock tae caa.

'An ne'er a shot in aa the pack!
An fan I wad, the lass I'll tak
Wull hear aa day the croudlin o the dou.
My bonnie Mirren, fain I'd be
Gin ye wad tak a gift frae me:
Gowd hae I neen, my jo, tae gie;
But this neowe-kerven tass o wuid's for you.'

He said nae mair, but frae his pyoke
He dreuch, as 't war his haly Buik,
A bicker out o birk-wuid futtl't gleg;
For eident Allan likit weel
Sat on a steen, tae wark wi skeel:
In hours o ease this knacky chiel
Cud mak rare plaiks wi jist a jockteleg.

His pawkie hann cud kerve perjink
Wi eeriorums buskit dink
Craamills tae caa his hirsel throu the nicht;
An on their wuiden bells ilkeen,
An on the claps o glentin been,
He'd mak braa patrens mony een,
Flouers, gin he list, or birdies, fasson't richt.

But sic a tass as Allan brocht,
A hird-loun's gully never vrocht!
Ye wadna trou, I'se warran, gin ye saa.
Aa roun the rim his futtle seer
Hed shap't a bonnie flouerin brier,
An for the luggies, twa reid deer
Amo the wallant roses wannert slaa.

Laicher a wee, there kyth't a threesome
O denty kimmers, jimp an leesome.
A hird-loun slept ablow an aik nearhann.
The randy jillets, tapper-tae,
Cam creepin up tae faar he lay –
Een stappit in his mou for play
A chirry frae the ruskie in her hann.

An swythe the dovert laddie waukt,
An wi the lichtsome cutties laucht:
Een, ye'd hae thocht, wes browden jist a wheen.
The feegurs kyth't tae steir an meeve:
That they war vrocht an didna leive,
The birk-reet's fite aleen cud preive:
Nae drap nor skirp hed tasht the spang-neowe sheen.

Said Mirren: 'Weel, my kind hird-lad,
Trowth war I fain o sic a wad –'
She tuik a scance, but swythe lap back a spang:
'But I hae frae my ain lad dear
A braaer gift: his luve, I sweir!
A glent frae'm sets my hert asteir:
I'm stounin fair wi luve's owermaisterin stang!'

An lik an eemach she's awa.
Allan, wi dowie staps an slaa,
His tass pat by, trail't throu the gloamin dim;
Sair tribbel't wi the dauntonin thocht
That yon sweet loesome lass he'd socht
Cud hae for some loun, in her aucht,
Sae muckle luve tae gie – but nae for him!

Ian McDonough

LIFE IN THE GARDEN

It has long been my belief that proper respect for a person's powers of observation is one true mark of a civilised society. These days, sadly, no-one seems to notice anything anymore. Let me give you an example – you may be aware that in the centre of our capital city there stands a large, somewhat hysterically-styled stone structure. It is dedicated, I believe, to an early historical fantasist, and has in the passage of time acquired an appropriately disreputable look. It may well surprise you to learn that in the last three years this monument has moved some fifteen yards to the east. I know – I have measured it. My opinion has always been that excitability in architectural design is a dangerous thing.

As someone who prides himself in paying careful attention to the duties of citizenship, I felt obliged to report this occurrence to the proper authorities. After some onerous research into the responsibilities of the myriad outposts of local governance, I was able to locate the correct department, and armed with meticulously detailed charts and calculations, I put the salient facts to the relevant official. He confessed to having been unaware of this singular circumstance, but hazarded the opinion that perhaps the monument was intent on reaching the seafront at Portobello in order to wash itself free of the substantial coating of grime which had adhered to its outer surfaces. This struck me as a rather fanciful notion, and I was about to advise the man on the hazards of ill-considered speculation, but pressing official business appeared to weigh heavily on his mind, and he left in some haste. It is an unfortunate fact in these hurly-burly times of ours that few people seem to be granted the space to benefit from a leisurely and stimulating exchange of knowledge.

But I digress. As I have said, people these days notice so little, a shortcoming which may be viewed as relatively minor when compared to spoiling one's children or defrauding the revenue-collecting bodies. I have discovered from personal experience, however, that the consequence of this sadly almost-universal failing can be distressing in the extreme.

There can be few more vital ingredients of a settled and harmonious lifestyle than the detached bungalow. My own, inherited from my dear parents, is a fine example of the genre. Neither dull nor ostentatious, it stands at a respectable yet not unfriendly distance from its neighbours, and has, I fancy, an aura of respectability which stops short of stuffiness, being enlivened by a fine display of minor Victorian sculpture in the front garden. Inside, I have added little to the decorative scheme created by my late mother, other than to introduce some prints of Brueghel the Elder, of whom I am rather fond. Apart from the usual functional rooms, there is an admirable small study where I spend much of my time. The window of this room looks over a part of the garden where the tea-roses used to be situated. It was these very roses, in point of fact, which first began to manifest the rather striking formations that led to so much bother.

What can I say about the day they began to sing? The morning had suffered from a series of rather blustery showers blown across the city from the North Sea, but as the day pro-gressed a pleasant summer haze won through, and the late afternoon found me seated on a garden chair, poring over some old sporting annuals I had uncovered in the attic. My condition as a child had precluded any form of sporting activity, or indeed much contact of any description with others of my own age, but how I used to relish these deeds of daring on the soccer field. My reverie was interrupted after some time by what I imagined to be an inconsiderate neighbour playing their radio a touch too loudly; perhaps Mrs Aggater who is troubled with her hearing. But the music had a quality quite unlike anything I had previ-ously encountered on the radio, being produced not by any instrument of the orchestra, but rather by a wordless though quite expressive humming. I often hum to myself of a morning, and recognised the sound quite easily.

Rising from my chair, I strolled casually round the perime-ter of the garden, thus affording myself the opportunity to inspect both adjacent gardens. Nothing out of the ordinary could be attributed to these sources, and I was in the process of returning to my seat to mull the problem over, when the source of the enigma became only too apparent. My tea-roses, or at least some of them, were humming quietly to themselves. What is more, I could recognise the tune as being an air from the light opera called 'Patience', which I recall my father enjoyed greatly. I am, of course, aware than an occurrence such as this might lead many people to doubt the veracity of their senses. But I have trained myself over many years to apply a careful scientific approach in interpreting all of life's events, and I immediately set about conducting an empirical investigation into this singular phenomenon.

My first step was to fashion a pair of ear-plugs out of moist cotton-wool. On inserting these I found the humming to cease immediately, and I admit some relief at being able to eliminate the possibility that the sound was emanating from inside my own head. I then located a polythene bag, and placed it over one of the loudest of the roses. The volume did indeed become muted, but was still audible. Finally, I fetched my secateurs, and snipped the head off one of the singing blooms. I carried it indoors and placed it in a glass of water, where it continued to hum for some minutes but grew steadily more quiet. Eventually it lapsed into silence. Shortly afterwards, as the sun set over Corstorphine Hill, all the roses became quiet.

What was I to make of this? No botanical treatise familiar to me had made any reference whatsoever to sound-producing flora, not even among the more exotic Amazonian species, some of which apparently have limited powers of movement and rudimentary digestive tracts. No-one of my acquaintance had ever mentioned such a possibility in the course of conversation. Could it be they had simply not noticed?

During the evening, I mulled over the available facts, examining them from every angle. At last, I narrowed the possible explanations down to two: either the ability of certain species to vocalise had been unaccountably overlooked, or for some reason the roses in my garden had developed their remarkable attribute in isolation.

A further occurrence later that evening forced me to discount both theories. After prolonged periods of strenuous thought, it is frequently appealing to me to take some air and at the same time inspect my vegetable patch for signs of pests. This evening was no exception, and the night proved balmy and clear. I had just satisfied myself that the broccoli was indeed free from invasion, when I became aware of a soft but chirpy whistling. I immediately suspected an intruder, and went back into the kitchen to fetch a torch and a stout stick. On returning I plied the torch beam up and down the rows of carrots, peas and broad beans, but found myself quite unable to detect the presence of anyone else. Still the whistling continued, and to my utter amazement, I was able to narrow down the source to the potato-patch. My potatoes were whistling! Furthermore, the tune could clearly be discerned as none other than 'Colonel Bogey', another old favourite of my departed father. Taking up a pitchfork, I uprooted one of the potato-plants and brought it indoors. As with the rose, the whistling continued from some minutes; indeed it became rather irritating as the tune is a basic one and does not stand up well to constant repetition. Eventually, like the rose, it ceased, although I could still hear its compatriots of the potato-patch keep up the refrain in the garden.

Sleep that night proved elusive, as my mind raced from one theory to the next. While it was just possible to accept that gardeners the world over had failed to become aware of the humming properties of tea-roses, this theory was more difficult to apply convincingly to potatoes. After all, the noise produced by a large field of commercially-grown whistling potatoes would surely be impossible to miss. Yet it was equally difficult to accept that both my roses and my potatoes had simultane-ously, and independently of all the other examples of their species, developed such remarkable musical powers. I tossed and turned, all the while being only too conscious of the muted strains of 'Colonel Bogey' from the back garden.

As the dawn arrived at five-thirty am, I rose from my bed and donned dressing-gown and slippers. Gingerly, I opened the kitchen door: the whistling had subsided. Outside, I walked along the rows of vegetables, half-expecting at any time a fresh display of aberrant behaviour, but finding things in order I took the paved path round to the front lawn. The neighbour-hood was wrapped in a comfortable silence, broken only by the odd snatch of early birdsong, a pleasing and wholly unre-markable sound. Alas, any thoughts of the re-establishment of nature's order were soon dismissed. An unmistakable whisper-ing was beginning to issue from the grass below my feet.

At first I could not make out specific words, but by crouch-ing low and applying my ear to the turf, I was soon able to discern the abhorrent content of this peculiar conversation, and almost began to doubt my own sanity. Although it is now many years since I have heard them, the voices of my father and mother could clearly be made out, whispering to each other in urgent tones. The content of their speech, however, was one entirely alien to anything they would have uttered in their life-time, consisting largely of the most brazen sexual innuendo, interspersed with noises which I can only describe as animalistic. I flatter myself that my mental composure is of a high order, but this was too much. I strode out to the greenhouse, replaced my slippers with a pair of green wellington boots, and picked up a spade. Working furiously, I cut the entire lawn into square sections, then lifted up each section and replaced it face down. The lawn is not small, and this operation took some time, but by nine am the task was completed. I was distressed to observe that a small band of curious neighbours had assembled at the garden-gate, but consoled myself with the knowledge that I had achieved my objective: the lawn had ceased to whisper.

Exhausted by my labours, I returned to bed and slept fitfully until the early afternoon. On rising again, I made myself some tea and toast and considered the events of the previous twenty-four hours. I had to admit that I was badly shaken, and although in normal circumstances I pride myself on an inquiring intellect, I felt that these bizarre manifestations were beginning to threaten my equilibrium. Without further ado, I ventured outdoors and dug up every last potato-plant and tea-rose, burning them all in a bonfire.

That evening in my study, I treated myself to a fine old Amontillado and once again reflected upon these unusual happenings. Gradually, I began to feel that I might have been somewhat hasty in disposing of these singular specimens so summarily. Even though the specimens were now irremediably destroyed, should the fact of their inexplicable behaviour not be reported to the proper authorities? After all, if similar plants existed, as yet unnoticed, a rigorous scientific survey was clearly in order. In the case of the grass, there was further impetus for research, as further examples of such foul behaviour would constitute a significant threat to public order.

Early the next morning I telephoned the Royal Botanical Gardens, and after much unnecessary debate, secured an appointment with a senior botanist for that very afternoon. Due to the effects of a hasty luncheon, I found myself rather out of sorts as I set off in the appropriate direction, a feeling compounded by the antics of an extremely rude child who dogged my steps for some distance, whistling tunelessly all the while. The situation became even more intolerable when he was joined at a road-junction by a fellow child who also began to whistle. I did, of course, ignore this ill-bred display, but was brought to a sudden halt when the previously unstructured melody was abandoned and replaced by 'Colonel Bogey'. I immediately demanded that they tell me if they had heard my potatoes whistle. To my great annoyance, the wretched creatures turned tail and ran before I could establish any details.

The Botanical Officer was a shabby little man who appeared far from pleased to receive a visit. It was on my mind to point out his status as a public servant, but I desisted, proceeding instead to give him a full and detailed account of my experiences. He fell silent for some time, but then asked for and carefully recorded my name and address, assuring me that he would indeed notify the appropriate authorities. I replied that I had assumed myself to be in the presence of the appropriate authorities, but he stated that this matter was well outside his particular field. Realising that I was clearly wasting my time, I took my leave and returned, rather disappointed, to my bungalow.

For a few days following this, my previous uneventful existence seemed to re-establish itself, and all in the garden was quiet. One wet Tuesday morning shortly afterwards, however, I woke to a dreadful clamour, and fearing the worst, ventured into the garden to investigate. This time the very ground itself was the cause of the disturbance. Whistling, tuneless singing, cries, moans and snatches of conversation were all at once rising from the earth. The volume was so great I knew that I must act instantly if the whole neighbourhood was not to be disturbed. I immediately began to dig at the offending soil, guessing that these distressing acoustic properties would extend no farther than the top three feet or so. With a great deal of strenuous effort I managed to turn the soil over until the cacophony subdued down to a barely-audible murmur, and I returned, badly shaken and exhausted, to the house.

My victory was temporary. The following day I discovered the beautiful garden, so beloved of my parents in happier days, once more filled with sound. I am now obliged to spend the greater part of my waking hours toiling to bury ever anew the noisy ground. Often, I find myself wishing that someone, the authorities, a neighbour, or passer-by perhaps, would notice my plight, but people notice so little these days. Besides, I live in fear of digging too deeply.

James McGonigal

QUICK NOTE

Alison it wasn't you yesterday I thought I saw astonishing
the crowd in Cumbernauld Town Centre. You were fuller faced
and obviously pregnant, your hair drawn back into its usual coil
now a mere foil to this other bump. And of course there's you
looking limitlessly content, though freighted also with two
bulging plastic bags from Tescos.
                                     It wasn't you I realised –
only an enceinte easy-oasy angel that turned my head before
I shook it clear. Do you have somewhere (here) a smiling
slightly waddling doppelganger, or dark twin breasting
the Saturday waves in our plaza's plateglass pool?
                                      Between Dixons green
infinities of screens and the brown hot rolls stretched out on
Dalziels baking trays like Spaniards on their playa
I watched you glide on past into the future. You
and whoever. Ever. Blessings + love. Yours.

SEEING THE LIGHT

of aurora borealis bamboozlingly far south
last night as we drove to our evening class
under a sky the colour of blood oranges

that pulsed as if the fruit could fizz
through pith and rind and then inhale
again to perfect segments

as if a doctor's hand had moved
under the flesh of air to turn
the unsuspecting foetus of a star.

A brightness where the pain of many prayers
was anchored. The Firth of Forth opened
and closed its mouth at this orange walk

across the sky beyond the high flats –
where folk like us, housekeeping in infinity,
tapped out their codes, tapped out and in

their testament of clothed and naked lights.

Hugh McMillan

THE SUM OF HUMAN KNOWLEDGE

Ron Cormack, me and Shaun from Orkney were always the backbone of the Royal Vic's Quiz Team. There were others that drifted in now and then, mostly perpetual student types, but they weren't in it properly, for the right reasons. They came along, showed off a bit, then left saying things like 'it's only a bit of fun' or 'it's just a night out with a few pints, that's all'. It wasn't a bit of fun to Ron, me and Shaun. We worked at it. We had to. We weren't what you would call good scholars. We would spend most nights at the snug in the Royal Vic reading up on everything we could get our hands on. Compendiums of knowledge, atlases, surveys of great scientific discoveries of the 20th century. We would read them out, write them down. Sometimes we understood them but if we didn't we wrote them down anyway and learned them off by heart. That's what we did with the Doppler Effect, learned it off by heart after five pints of Old Jock with a Karaoke Session raging round about us. Any book we couldn't get Shaun would nick for us. Shaun was the world's finest shoplifter. It was how he made his living. He would go into the pub in the morning, take orders and, in spite of the fact he was usually already well gassed by mid-day, return within the hour with the required goods, size 4 children's boots, or the latest Arnold Schwarzenegger video, or a particularly complex type of fishing fly. Christ alone knows how he did it, the man was so obviously steaming, so dressed like a tramp, that you would think the store detectives would have done a number on him before he got a shoe in the door. He was not the kind of man you could imagine blending into the background in the Fancy Goods Department. When Shaun wasn't working he was talking in that thick accent about the mother who dumped him here in Dumfries years ago, or about his particular love, the Stuart Kings of Scotland. He knew everything there was to know about the Stuart Kings, James IV's shoe size, the number of rivets that held the Great Michael together and so on. He talked about the Stuart Kings as if he'd seen them that morning. One of the great moments in his life was when he was in Edinburgh, a witness in a murder trial in the High Court, and he'd come face to face with a stained glass portrait of James IV. He would tell you about it when he was really out of his head, like other folk would confide their inner-most desires. 'There he fookin wass' he would say, his eyes closed, 'Jams the fookin forth, the man eeself, lookin at me' and he would sit and nod his much scarred head till he fell asleep or plunged out into the night to find somewhere to sleep.

Ron, on the other hand, knew most about rivers, lakes and so on. I don't want to be cruel about Ron because I loved my quiz team like a family, but Ron had a lot of problems. He was almost a dwarf, had a hump on his back and the most hair of anyone I'd ever seen. I reckoned he was trying to hide behind it. He had hair half way down his back and a huge bushy beard. Ron knew all about geography. He knew the height of K2 to the exact centimetre, all the cities on the Danube, the biggest freshwater lake in Malawi and so on. He'd known these things forever, that was an impressive thing, since he was a wee boy.

Ron and Shaun were great men to have on your side in the bitter crucible that was the south Dumfries winter Pub League, not only because of what they knew but also because they were well known around town for being able to handle themselves. Well, more accurately, they were well known round town for being mad bastards. For that reason no-one ever cheated us, tried to give themselves half marks for wrong answers, or tried to cook the books afterwards. At the start of the season there had been a mild dispute in the Poachers Rest about the answer to the question 'Why do some warm blooded mammals hiber-nate in Winter?'. Suffice to say, Shaun stuck the head in the opposing team captain and the barman, and the barmaid, before the game was abandoned. Ron had been barred from most pubs in Dumfries and was only allowed in for the dura-tion of the 80 questions of the Quiz. Then he went back to the Royal Vic where they looked after their own. It was like home there.

As for me, I just loved knowing things. So when some bas-tard looked through you in the street as though you were shit or someone in a shop didn't serve you till they'd seen to all the folk in nice coats you could say something like 'what's the Native American name for Bigfoot?' and they'd stare at you, or bluster, but you'd know you'd put one over on them and they'd be angry that there was some little way in which you were more perfect than them. Knowledge is power, as I said to the boys. If we knew everything, there would be nothing to worry about ever again.

Our great enemies in the League were a team of teachers called Lokomotif Marchmount. They toured round all the pubs doing quizzes, mostly for cash. They were bald but they thought they were it. We played them once, about a year before in some one-off, and they tanked us but it was before we got our ideology and when our team still had middle class wanks of students who insisted on answering, wrongly, for all of us. It was before we became a unit, honed to perfection in the cause of knowledge. As we carved a triumphant swathe through our enemies it must have been clear to them that we had been reborn. Our last match of the season was against Marchmount. We were virtually equal in points going into it. It was to be held at Clarence's, a shitey reconstructed pub/wine bar where we could be assured of a hostile atmosphere. I gathered the lads together at lunchtime to make sure there were no surprise breenges into cheap sherry or pills and we sat and drank sweet tea, reeling off the sum total of human knowledge. At 7.30 we went in, Shaun got stuck into the Old Jock, and Ron was given the strict conditions for his presence, as usual. We sat down and looked the teachers coolly up and down. They were looking balder, but no cleverer than before. The first round was History, a piece of pish, the only wrong answer being mine when I thought the Tang Dynasty ruled China in 260 BC. It was the Shin. 'Sorry lads' I said, but we were four points ahead and they were looking rattled. Next was Geography. You could sense Ron smiling somewhere under that beard. He knew the length of Lake Nyasa, the height of the Angel Falls and the English translation of the capital of Outer Mongolia. They didn't. Seven points clear and you could see the sweat on their pates. We were cruising. Shaun was smiling, Ron was pleased as punch. The following round was General Knowledge. First question was the name of a dwarf horse from prehistoric times. Ron bristled a bit but we got it OK. Hippocampus. Then they asked us about the Japanese art of growing dwarf trees. I was calming Ron down so we missed the point. When they asked us to write the names of the Seven Dwarfs Ron snapped and attacked the question master with a tin tray. It took four of them to throw him out. Then things went from bad to worse. Still, we were two points ahead going into the drinks interval but just before the final round the police mysteriously arrived and arrested Shaun for having in his possession 46 pork chops from Marks and Spencers. When the fuss died down I sat by myself and looked at the bastards opposite. They were grinning now. The whole thing had been a set up. I sat and drank all the drinks left on the table, staring at them, answering when I could and when we were at the final question and they were five points ahead I went up, pushed the boy aside, and took the mike.

'Tell me this,' I said, "What's the fucking meaning of life?'

They looked hard at each other and one of them said in a whisper, 'It doesn't matter, we win anyway.'

'Exactly,' I said, then walked out into the rain.

GLASGOW TOILET WALL, PARTIALLY CLEANED

This is the place to wink.
I have a footlong rick.
Dress in laddies kickers?
Have a hairy vest?
My first tim was god,
gave godhead.
I need a gorgous honk.

Meet you at 9 o'cock.

Gordon Meade

From the Sequence
FLOTSAM AND JETSAM

The footprints start at the head of the stone
steps that lead down to the beach. It is only then
that they begin to deepen, to make an impression
on sand. From time to time, I lose them, fragmenting
over seaweed-covered rocks, dissolving into pools.
Head-down, I do not hope for any destination, yet still
am dismayed to see them disappear at the water's edge.

*

Looking for her in the first
black and white photograph of her,
an image through ultrasound, is a waste
of time. I have known her only in full colour,
from the moment she emerged, with her
flaming hair, from the dark room of her mother.

*

She eats her trout by using its head
as a fork, by lifting the lightly grilled
pieces of flesh to her mouth in its own teeth.
After we have cleared away her plate, she tells us
that the trout, its head, its bones, and the flesh
she swallowed, all swam back to the sea.

*

She wants me to walk her up the hill;
past the molehills and rabbit holes;
past the thistles and the songs of grass-
hoppers; to the summit and the thrush's anvil.
Around it lie the remains of snails' shells.
Having seen them, and a heron flying above
the farmer's field, she asks to be carried downhill
on my shoulders, to feel the wind in her hair.

Gus Morrison

HEALTHY EATING

What's on the menu the night, then?
Dinners.
What's your favourite dinner?
I don't know
I suppose it depends, really
on how I feel.
Like it might be a carry oot curry
frae the Indian in Kilbowie Road
Chicken Tikka Achari bubbling hot
with green chillies and garlic
and methi cloves ginger and spices
Indian vegetables, Nan bread,
mixed pakora and Chicken Chaat
for starters washed down with the
coldest bottled beer straight from the fridge
or else it might be sausage, bacon and eggs
Free range eggs and Canadian bacon
with Marks and Spencers butcher's style
sausages sizzling or even pork links
from Rogers the Butcher frae Duntocher
(no chance of E Coli there)
Sometimes a totty scone and a bit
of black pudding help to fill any gaps on the plate
Other days it has to be a fish supper
standing ootside up the toon
the fish done in crispy batter chips piping hot
the onions hard and crisp and tasty from Gold Star
bought from the best chippy in Glesga
which remains a secret
coz the queue is long enough
served by a wee Italian woman
who lets on she canny speak a word
o' English although she's
been in Glasgow since the forties
the portions here are huge
the fish breaks in your hands
and melts on the tongue hot and delicate

producing gasps of delight and mutterings
of sheer ecstasy
But
this is thirsty work
and needs a large carton of hot tea in polystyrene or
a bottle of chilled Irn Bru
or both.

Michael Munro

COCKTAIL HOUR

The guy in front in the dawn bus queue
nudged my elbow
and my head rose out of the *Herald*.
Hands in pockets, pointing with a nod,
'Cheers!' he said, and winked.
Eyes following, I saw
the full gold round of the morning moon
caught on the rim
of a Red Road towerblock,
a lemon slice on a tall glass.
I pantomimed a toast to earn his grin
and got back down to situations
vacant.

Joe Murray

STERRHEID HAIKUS

1.
seven steps tae a close
wan door
'nither door
the smell ih pie & beans

2.
hauf
brick
nth
crash
ih
broken
g
   l
      e
  s
     s
pensioner mugged
fuhr 10 pee

3.
hauf wan
seturday mornin
nae sterrheid light
juist the smell ih
stale
p
 i s
s   s
  s
    s
      h h
    h h
      h
       !
    !
  !

4.
big rod (blastin)
fit stompin tae
patsy cline, nthi
dj's wurk shifts

5.
awakened
to YOUR warmth
3 small ki ss es
morning ellipsis

JEANETTE

From a fitful sleep   I
struggle to wake.   You
are there   lying
head raised
on one hand   smiling.
Slowly you stretch   kiss me
the bad night gone
I murmur   good mornings

William Neill

Thrie Sonnets frae Giuseppe Belli (1791–1861)

THE GAUMMLER'S WIFE

Listen, dearie, I'm gey near in despair;
for want o sleep ye'll think me haurdly wyce,
syne he gaed wud wi playin cairds an dice
this tash o Matha gart me bide hairt-sair.

Yon wee bit tocher I had hained 's nae mair,
as if it had been burned ti pleisure him;
an see the hoose, the place is gey near tuim
haurdlie a buird ti sett at, or a chair.

And Mary Mither, jist the ither nicht
I laid thare waukin in the wee smaa oors,
he cam ben wi nae jaikit ti his name.

Whit fashes me mair nor yon sorry sicht –
here's me richt heavy nou while he still poors
awa sic siller as wad hap the wean.

gaummler: gambler   tash: blemish   Matha: Mathew
gart me bide: caused me to remain   tocher: dowry
hained: saved   tuim: empty   buird: table   ben: indoors
fashes: worries   heavy: pregnant   siller: money
hap: wrap   wean: child

THE NICHT O DREID

Ye're no gaun oot again – mad et yon lot?
Whit reid-wud norie's rettlin in yir heid?
I ken ye're thenkin on some bluidie deed
wi yon black gullie in ablo yir coat!

Billy lad, dinnae gae aff in sic a state;
ye're aff ti you flash pub, nou dinna lee!
pit doun that dirk or see's it ower ti me.
For Jesus sake jist lat thaim gang their gaet.

Gin ye gae oot, I's no be bydin here
whan ye get hame. Stab *me* nou! Dinnae swither!
but I'll staun here until ye drap yon knife.

I dinna want oor bairn that's sleepin thare
ti wauken up the morn athoot a faither,
in some daft vennel-stushie twined o life.

reid-wud: plain crazy   norie: idea   gullie: large knife
gang thair gaet: go off   bydin: remaining   swither: hesitate
vennel-stushie: backstreet brawl   twined: deprived

PAIP LEO

Afore Paip Genga* gaed ti his lang hame,
crined ti a gowpenfu o cauld hambanes,
ye'd hear him ruised alang the causey-stanes:
better for us nor winnin the Lotto Game.

Never yae thing he did that ye micht blame
never said ocht that didnae mak guid sense,
his faes were nocht but skellums waantin mense,
thieves, convicks, orra tinks had a better name.

But scarce he'd slippit aff whan suddenlie
the blissid Paip had vainist at great speed
intil a cuddie, a tod, a daft auld shite.

An the clishmaclavers stack til the puir man tae:
jist as the mice dae whan the auld cat's deid –
they haud a ceilidh an dance atour his kyte.

*Leo XII (della Genga) 1823–29.

crined: shrank   gowpenfu: handful   ruised: praised
causey-stanes: pavement   yae: one (single thing)
ocht: anything   faes: foes   skellums: rascals
mense: honour   orra tinks: coarse persons   cuddie: donkey
tod: fox   clishmaclavers: gossip   ceilidh: a party
atour: around, on top of   kyte: belly

David Nicol

FLITTING

Time was for me
when flitting
meant packing a rucksack
and calling a cab,
leaving no trace
but a note saying,
Keep the deposit
in lieu of last
fortnight's rent.

Whereas today
a flit means a
removal van, mail to
be redirected,
and a summer enquiring
into the nature of
mortgages, carrying
the burden of capital
on my back.

Liz Niven

Extracted Fae
A DRUNK WUMMAN SITTIN OAN A THISTLE
(misquoted is a'body's property)

The pink jaggy bunnet o Scotland
Wee an sherp an jags ma bum
Best jist no tae sit on him.

We should hae kent fae Picts tae Punks
Tae no daur meddle wi him an his spunks!
Yer toorie's gallus, yer spikes feel sherper
Hae ye pitten on yer Doctor Martins?

Or is this thistle menopausal,
Growin auld nae seeds tae scatter?
Never!

Here let me join ye this starry night
Up here on the hill A'm fu... o delight.

Wee thistle ye've mair life tae lead,
Tho an ancient lass ye've bairns tae feed.

Or mibbe ye're sufferin PMT?
Never mind ye'll soon be free.
The tension ower the votes aw coontit,
Wir Parliament formed, the right wing routit.

Nae sleepin oot in cairdboard boxes
We'll burn a bonfire wi thir hoaxes.
Private beds, opt oot scuils,
Toffy noses, boolmoothed fools.

Tae climb this hill will be wir aim,
An celebrate by next Beltane.

A amna fou sae muckle as drunk ... drunk dry ... totally drained

Talkin o seats ma ain's fair sair
Ye'll say A'm talkin throu it!
A'm awfie 'in yer face' in fack
An surely gan tae rue it.
Plenty tae rue bit mair tae delight in
How many wumman this nicht will be labourin?
Millions o wumman bring forth in pain
An every bairn is aye worth haein
An tae every wumman every bairn
Is as muckle as Christ, it gans wi'oot sayin.

Tae be a wumman – an tae hae aw men's equal richts
Nae harder job tae wumman is in sight
So Emily Pankhurst an Florence o the Lamp
Joan o Arc an wimmen in the auld Faslane Peace Camp
A'll toast yer memory, lie still in yer graves
The fight gans oan, we're yet makin waves

So here's tae the sisters whose names have been shrunk
Tae the size o apprentice tae husband's great wurk

Tae Willa translator with Edwin her man
Who brought Kafka's darkness tae light wi her hand
Or Bertold Brecht's mistress who still tae this day
Was mibbe the wan whae gave birth tae a play?
These marriages fine or lovers entwined
Were addin thir seed o a lit'rary kind.

An curse tae the day when George Eliot thought
That a lassie's real name wid ruin the lot.
An even tae nou in millenium years
Dae we need wimmen's books and anthologies here?
Can we staun wi the men? Can we aw hae a jar?
A still meet ma pal ootside o the bar!
Or a tearoom we'll find insteid o a pub
An are wimmen welcome doon at your club?

A thistle, A'm stertin tae stagger A'll hae tae sit doon
Ma brain's gettin addled under this moon
Ma dander's got up, A'm jist in full flight.
The drink maks ye blether an blether aw night.

Ah thistle woe is me
Ye couldnae mak a wee cup o tea?
Tae quench ma thirst
Thon alcohol jist leaves ye drouthie
Ma een aw red ma poems get couthie

An whaur's yer love lines ye'll be wunnerin?
Does yer thochts no turn tae romance?
Does the drink no mak ye frisky?
Ye ken the situation though
Wumman like thon ur considered risky.

Bit a man's a real man gin he's writin
Aboot or daein the physical.
Bit thon kinna wumman's jist a slut
An should only write clean lyricals.

Could ye jist hae seen the history books if Rabbie wis a lass?
She'd o fun hersel wi child, cut aff at the first pass
                              An wrote nae poems,
An nivver hid the chance tae write like Rantin Rovin Rabbie,
Who didnae try tae pen a poem while stuck at hame wi babbie.
                              Or write in Habbie.

An doon the sweep o centuries
Can ye list the artists' names?
The heroines and writers
The painters who wir dames?

Naw! Well no as many
As there shuid be anyway.
My, is it no jist grand whit a wee dram can dae?
It maks ye rhyme,
*   – an talk sense tae!*

Wheesht! Can ye hear them cry doon in the Common?
Girnin folk. Men an wimmen!

Drums in the Walligate, pipes in the air
Aw the lassies cryin that it isnae fair

Bit it's no as it used tae be gin Grieve wis a loon
In Langholm or onie o the Border toons.

The bearer twirls her earrings an gowd bracelet
Fair as Roses her skin is set

A five-fit lassie wid wallop a punch
Wi her young bosom buddie she has a hunch

That if her an her sisters hae onie say
There'll be nae thriepenny bits minted the day

New pennies then ecus hiv replaced the siller
New Scotland will no be selt doon the river

An A'll dance the nicht wi the stars in heaven
Fir lassies ye're right the future's bidden

Nae mair relegations tae ootside the tent
Doffin yer caps tae the men history lent
Superiority jist fir a whyle.
So sup wi me sisters an gie us a smile
Ye'll ride wi the rest at the Common Riding Day
And form Constitutions up Parliament way

Society will warm wi wir mitherin guid
We'll shair oot the wealth an aw hae fine food

Tae hell wi the blueness o each tae his ain
Let's reborn this kintra fir oor dochters' weans.

There, A'm away again. A'm jist becomin a right wee pain.
A'd better get sober afore A gan hame
Or the neebours will talk an blacken ma name.
Get doon aff yer soapbox! *Ma man wid be shouting*
Bit you ma freen thistle jist patiently listen.

Ay, thistle, whit's wir future?

We'll speak wi a voice that is common bit smert
Gaelic and Scots and English – the lot!
We'll ken whaur we cam frae an whaur we ur gan
We'll aw hae a say each wumman an man

Democracy lives, Socialism's no deid
Tho there's plenty will argue we're saft in the heid
An talkin o heids ma ain's gien me gyp
The drink's wearin aff it's near time fir a kip

A flattened the thistle, ma frock's nane the waur,
An A ken that this flooer will no be sae faur
Fae springin back up tae its full magic height.
It's made o strang smeddum A've seen that this night

Way up on the hill here the sterns fir ma freens
The drink maks ye blether an talk o yer dreams.
Bit we hae tae keep dreamin or ocht we'll aw dee,
Ma sisters ma brithers ma Thistle an me.

But yince John kens whit A've been through
The nicht, A dinna doot it,
He'll ope his airms in welcome true,
And clack nae mair aboot it...

Sae cheery bye ma thistle freen
As doon the brae we go.
An thanks fir bein a listenin lug
Tae a wumman daft an fou.

Tak ma advice fir whit it's wirth
An tae yersel be true
Tho A'm in ma cups it's still gey clear,
We daurna meddle wi you.

Martin Osler

JIMMY

I said to him, I said,

'Jimmy you're a man now and it hurts. It fucking hurts bad. It hurts because you have to get a job, because you're drifting apart from your pals cause they've got to find work too, because something is on your shoulders that wasn't but a year ago. I remember Dad mentioned it, I think... responsibility. That's a big word for a wee guy from a council estate but Jimmy, it's a word and it speaks to everyone, whether they take it on board or no.

You don't know how it creeps up on you and suddenly there it is, ya bastard, how did you get there? It's a bloody burden but you carry it to the grave.

You know you're lucky. Ma and Dad are still together, you've got something to fall back on so to speak, and you know they'd catch you.

Are you listening, Jimmy, are you? Because I don't think you hear me right. There's people who are really alone, really... eh?'

But Jimmy digs his toes deeper into the sand, pushing them in until there are no more toes.

Jimmy likes to hide. He was really good at it too when we were young and played kick-the-can and hide-and-seek. He was so good that he hid for three hours one summer evening. It was pitch dark when Ma found him. She was seething, screaming his name all over the place. He said that he thought we were still playing but that was doubtful on account of it being pitch dark.

No, Jimmy just liked to be alone and that was what the problem was now that he did not want to be alone any more. There was no-one.

And he's only twenty-one. Just a lad still really. But I suppose like Dad keeps saying, back then they were men much younger than they are now. I don't really think that Jimmy needs to hear that sort of thing, but that is Dad, bellowing majestic statements and then leaving no room for any further debate on the matter.

Ma shakes her head and Jimmy's goes looking for nothing in his dinner.

'Jimmy, Jimmy! Are you listening? I can't say anything else can I? You've got to deal with this, it won't go away, it won't. I'm telling you it will get better. It did for me. I mean, eventually things work out and you look back and you smile because you were so daft back then.

'Just don't lose the place just now. I mean, don't do anything stupid like, you know...

'Billy's a cousin but he was damn stupid and now he's banged up. That's no good... robbing folk like.

'Look at me. I mean, I got a job at eighteen, worked a while, changed my job and now I'm earning great money. It worked out for me so it did. It'll work for you too, no problem. You're as good as me? Eh, Jimmy?

'Remember when you won that trophy for woodwork and Ma was so proud, talked about it for a month, all the neighbours in to see it and admiring it. Ma wasn't like that when I won my English prize. No way, that was nothing compared to that trophy. It was a gem though.'

I thought he smiled then but you never knew with Jimmy, he had a sort of contorted face that could change like the wind. One moment it was smiling, the next growling or whatever.

Mind you, it looked like he was smiling, but you never quite knew if he meant it. Used to cause us awful bother in the pubs. We'd be standing there, me, my pals and Jimmy and suddenly, out of nowhere, some guy would start shouting the odds. 'What are you looking at, smiling at my girlfriend like that?' And Jimmy wouldn't be smiling, it was just his face was like that. I would have to step in or big Bob or someone. Aye, Bob was handy.

But Jimmy, well, you never quite knew anything with Jimmy. What he was thinking I mean.

I remember one time when I fixed him up with this girl. She was pretty, not my type, but pretty and I thought Jimmy would like her. So off they went on a date to the pictures and it seemed to go OK. Then, when Ma and Dad went to bed he just turned on me. 'What the fuck did you set me up with that daft bitch for? Eh? Just stay out of my business in future will you?'

Well, I was surprised, I mean I only tried to help my wee brother out and the lassies are important at that age. You've got to get out and mingle and meet people and mess about a little. It's all experience and you have somebody to turn to when things are like they are now for Jimmy. It helps.

'Jimmy, got a bird at the moment, anyone special? Fuck, will you speak to me? We're meant to be having a conversation you know. Maybe that would help you, a girl, someone to talk to. You know, and the other, you know?'

And then, would you believe it, he says he's got a girl but it's not so smooth at the moment. Maybe that's why he's depressed. I mean girls are bad for that. They're great to have when you feel good and sometimes when you feel bad, but there are times when they sense that you feel bad and kind of stick the knife in. Almost to say that they know you're feeling bad and that you need them now, and they're going to twist the knife just so that you remember not to take them for granted. It's a good time to kick a man, when he's down. Women have that intuition. Aye and it works.

'What's her name, Jimmy? What? Her? That girl a couple of doors down? Bloody hell, she's worth hanging onto. Her dad works at Sullivan's, right? Aye, him.'

In fact I wasn't too sure that Jimmy was telling the truth about the girl from two doors down. Just something I felt. You know, a gut reaction. It might have had something to do with the fact that her father was one of the unfortunate guys to have fallen foul of my brother's stupidity in the past.

You see, Jimmy was a fair shot with an air gun and his bedroom window faced out from the back of our house towards the allotments behind.

These allotments were after the usual fashion, long strips of vegetables and flowers and whatever stretching back. There were also greenhouses dotted about at various intervals and a greenhouse meant wealth amongst the allotment guys. The other gardeners, of which our Dad is one, kind of respected the greenhouse owners. It may have had something to do with the fact that allotment owners neighbouring the greenhouse allotment were allowed, if the greenhouse owner was kept on side, to use his greenhouse to plant seedlings and house plants over winter.

Well, Dad's allotment neighboured the greenhouse allotment of Jimmy's bird's father from two houses down.

We had this game of seeing who could fire the air gun from the bedroom window and hit a watering can perched on an old brazier the men used to crowd around for warmth in the colder gardening months.

Jimmy was a grand shot and I was too, so we had some fair old competitions to see who could knock the can off first.

And this one time Jimmy's elbow slipped on the windowsill and he lost his aim and shattered three panes of glass in the greenhouse belonging to his bird's Dad.

Now, we could have hidden and said nothing but the guy just happened to be in the greenhouse tending to his tomatoes and that was that.

Dad lost his winter privileges and Jimmy's backside must have burned for a week.

'Do you remember that time when we blasted those windows with an air gun? Aye, how the hell did you get in with that bird after all the hassle we had then with her Dad? Yeh, she's a nice looking girl. Not unlike Marie you know, not unlike her in complexion, hair and stuff. Similar sort of walk as well, kind of. You like Marie, eh? She doesn't have a bad word to say about you. Always how's Jimmy, how's his job hunting going, has he met any nice girls yet? She's always asking after you. Sometimes think it's you she's after! She'll be pleased to hear about the new girl though.'

I was beginning to run out of things to say to the guy and that's not like me. I mean, here we are sitting down trying to have a conversation and I'm having a conversation, sure, with my fucking self.

His feet digging at the sand, it's driving me mad and he's just staring out to sea, out to nothing, vacant like.

We don't come here often, the beach I mean. Ma and Dad would bring us about twice a summer and it was great, especially when we got a real scorcher. The girls in their bikinis, me and Jimmy having a sand castle competition, messing about in the water.

Ma would sit on a towel applying loads of sun-cream and reading some romance book and Dad would sit there guzzling beers, wearing those elaborate shades that Uncle Jimmy gave him for his birthday. And then after a few, he would jump up and say, 'Right lads where's the football?' and start organising a game with some of the other Dads and sons on the beach. Those were often fired up occasions because Dad loved his football and he also loved his beer and common sense decrees that the two don't work together too well.

One time he dived in at this fat geezer who was showing a few skills out on the wing and Dad and geezer flew upwards and landed, all tangled in the sand. It took a couple of Dads to sort out the situation before it escalated. Then people started to drift off back to their towels and sun-cream, to hide behind their romance books. The perils of beach football.

Mind you, Jimmy was a good player. He played for the school and the church. We would watch him every Saturday and he was good. Dad reckoned he could go pro but I was never so sure about that. But like everything else, Jimmy seemed to lose interest and soon stopped playing. That was a shame though because he was a good player. Strong and quick and you need that.

Now, Uncle Jimmy, he was some player too apparently. Seems that he damaged his knee training, the week before he was due for a trial with a big English team. He's not so good now though. Put away for armed robbery. That's Billy's Dad by the way.

That happens though. A guy gets close to making it and then, in a stroke, he's back to nothing, it all goes downhill. Now that must break you bad.

I've not seen him for years now. Ma won't let us go to see him. I think she was scared some of it might rub off on me and Jimmy. Maybe.

'Jimmy, do you want to walk down the beach a bit, stretch the legs? I could do with a bit of a dander down to the water?'

We get up and walk down to the water and I feel the smell of the salt in my lungs rising up and down and stinging my throat. It feels fresh and relieving, so different to the city air. That gets into your lungs too but it suffocates you.

If you wanted to kill yourself you could do it here, so desolate and unending, the sea I mean, unending. You could just walk out there and never stop and the tide would take you away to America or someplace. Mind you, if you didn't time your walk right you were liable to get washed up in Larne or somewhere in Ireland.

Jimmy's still looking ahead but I know he feels the salt air too. I watch him taking deep breaths.

Do you know Jimmy had asthma? Well, aye, he does sort of. Sometimes he gets it in summer when there's lots of pollen

about and it stuffs him up and he takes deep breaths. That kind
of inhibited the football career a bit. Near the end of the season, April and May, Jimmy would be wheezing about the pitch
at the end of games. But he got one of those spray things and it
seemed to go away.

He's got problems, our Jimmy has, but he's a good lad and
I like him. He's my brother, of course I do, but we get along
well, I think.

So we walk further along the beach, me with my hands in
my pockets looking at him with his hands dangling by his
sides kind of helplessly, looking out to sea. But he can't dig his
feet into the sand anymore and that makes me feel better.

Soon, we reach the promontory and stop for another look
out to sea, from another angle, but it's just the same, endless
ocean.

So we turn and go back to where we were sitting before
and I notice it's nearly ten, we should be getting back.

'Jimmy, let's go back to the car, it's time to go, it's late now,
come on.'

But Jimmy says he wants to sit there for a while longer, but
I'm dying for a piss as well. You can only hold it in for so long.
So he says he'll stay while I drive to the public toilets and then
come back and pick him up at the top of the car park. But I'm
not so sure, I mean he's been acting pretty strange staring out to
sea and that and he's only said a couple of things all evening. It's
dark out there and unending. I mean, he wouldn't do anything,
but, well, Jimmy's not all there sometimes. You know the gun
and that, that nice lassie, he's not always got the top screwed
on. But he's my brother, what can I say. No, I'm not going
because I think you're going to kill yourself? I mean no way.

So I left and walked up the path to the car and I remember
thinking it was cold in there compared to outside and the
steering wheel was cold.

I told him, Jimmy, you're a man now and it'll hurt like hell
but we're all there for you and anything you need you know.
But I didn't know how much it hurt, I suppose. He was different, Jimmy, you know?

And I'll bet the sea was cold, I mean it looked fucking cold
from where I was looking.

Tom Pow

PILGRIM

When you arrive at the White Loch of Myrton,
that's not the end of your journey, though
for the time you are there it may seem so.

For the White Loch will say: lay it down,
why don't you? – the tired old rhetoric of self.
Contradiction, sophistry, hope or regret:

shove it all overboard like a lump
of machinery that's never quite made sense;
that's simply been something for you to work on.

Even now as it slips behind the scene,
the one you've called, 'White Loch of Myrton',
you feel how its arcane circuits absorb you.

But *you* are something altogether different,
sitting on a smooth rock-stool by the water's edge,
as so-slow bees drone between buttery blobs

of ragwort and trout click their watery tongues
whenever your back is turned. You are not
the heavy load you've cast from you. You share

instead something of the deep unruffled
stillness of the water, the bluish haze
of bulrushes, the load line between the trees

and their reflections. Hold to that lightness
and see how easy it is to love at the White
Loch of Myrton, where you have no history

but this moment. Still you'd be a fool
if you thought the White Swan of Myrton
would find any of this loveable in you.

And you were a fool to think you could love her.
Tending three dowdy chicks almost as big
as herself, she spits into your reverie:

Go refreshed, she says, but remember,
pilgrim, you cannot live forever on the edge
of the White Loch of Myrton.

MUSHROOMS

Today in the lee of the islands of Sherkin,
Castle, Calf, Clear and Hare, the small island
of Skeam East turns like a ragged butterfly
in a blue, wingless sea. Roaring Water Bay

can never have seemed so inaptly named.
In the fields above the island ruins, Dan and I,
the sun on our shirtless backs, pick mushrooms
in an idly purposeful way. They're everywhere,

extended families of milky white heads
shining in the summer's still cropped green.
And the houses, I ask – a scatter of stone husks
above the landside bay – when were they

abandoned? Hard to say: famine some; others
as late as the fifties. A hundred years or so
of a drifting death. I'm pulled to the island's
furthest edge, fooled by a handful of bone-

white crab shells. Water slaps into beaker-
smooth gulleys. An open boat chugs past, the dull
plops of lobster pots measuring the silence.
Together we fill a bucket with mushrooms

and cache them in a mesh of broken ferns;
then go off in search for more, strolling
aimfully through the open fields, leaving few
for those who'll come after. 'Shag 'em!'

I agree. Later as our families trail back
across the spit of land to where Dan's boat
tugs at the slightly less sandy beach, I idle
in a ruin, crouching below the rafters'

stone slots. The small windows have turned
from the landscape around them. Like a vegetable
beneath a box bed, I am brushed by the spores
of a shadow life the light can't touch.

That night our cornucopia of mushrooms
boils down into a mess of slippery ashes,
into the salty, blue-black ink of themselves.
Their juices colour everything they touch

with a fisherman's dye. It's the colour
of cold hearths, of a louring sky, of the grit
at the sea's edge after the storm has passed
and the Wreckers' eyes shine in the darkness.

Richard Price

As If

All your worries –
forget the lot
and hug me.

Hold's the word,
as if all's been said,
not yet done.

So don't listen to me
religiously.
Just

know I'm yours –
if it's talk, if love.
If love, love.

I Wish

'Let me down
in the bus bay?'

Hazard lights, idling,
wipers' tongues

dry, off. 'I,
I wish you well.'

'I wish *you* well.'

Actually holding hands.
'Friends?'

'You'll miss your.'
'I'll miss my.'

'I wish…
I wish.'

Sheila Puri

MIGRANT

When Devinder came along everyone was really happy. It helped that he was Jija-ji's[1] cousin. Jija-ji said that we would make a great couple. Still, mum and dad asked other people about him. They wanted to make sure their daughter would marry a good man. Once mum and dad were happy about him, the meeting was arranged between us. We first saw each other in my sister's front room which was reserved for special occasions. When I saw his eyes gently looking at me I felt a heat rush up through my body and I looked down at my feet. We met a few times before the wedding, usually by accident, when me and my sister-in-law were out shopping for the wedding. I'd see his face suddenly appear amongst the mass of activity in the bazaar, something inside me would jump. He usually was with a brother or cousin. Bhabi-ji[2] or his companion would say, 'Come I'll buy you a drink,' and then we'd go to the best taba in town – Heera's Taba[3]. We'd been going to Uncle Heera's since I was six. When the four of us would walk in he'd say loudly, 'come, come betia[4], come and sit here, pointing to the table which had the freshest bunch of flowers. And then he'd call the boys to make up milk badaam[5] with extra pistachio nuts and to bring freshly fried samosas. Sitting opposite my future husband I'd pull off bits of the samosa and the milk badaam could have been water. I was glad that Bhabi-ji was there. Bhabi-ji talked about places to visit in India and took charge of keeping everything going. In the noise and chatter of the taba I would feel safe and thrilled. Our eyes would look at each other and I'd see the longing that we both had to be alone. Then one of us would turn away worried that someone might see our secret. On the way back home Bhabi-ji would tease me. I would laugh and deny everything, but inside I bubbled over and the dusty street and hooting traffic just looked as if they all existed for me. But I often went from being happy to feeling tight in my stomach. I remember when I was alone, sitting on the doorstep, quite happily watching neighbours' children playing cricket. Their shouting interrupted my dreams. When they'd begin to squabble, they'd turn to me as the unofficial referee, 'Aunty, you saw it, what do you think? Be honest now,' shiny black eyes lit up with pleading and mischief. They'd carry on like this for a few minutes and when I wouldn't take sides they'd slowly return to their game. I'd watch them and the street with its different sellers shouting or neighbours waving as they went by, making remarks about my soon-to-be state of bridehood. The thought of being thousands of miles from everything I loved would make a hard and aching solid lump form inside me. So then I'd get up and make a start on the dahl dishes or whatever needed doing.

The wedding came. Gently and slowly we started to know each other. Sometimes we'd sit up till four in the morning, him telling me about his life and me talking about mine. Night-time was the only time we really had to be alone together. We were together for two weeks after our marriage. Devinder had to go back to Britain, he'd already stayed longer than his boss had allowed.

The plane journey made me stiff, sad and thrilled. Each minute taking me away from the only things I had known and loved but toward something new and exciting. After twelve hours I felt numbed and when I at last saw Devinder, I can't remember feeling anything. All I remember is the whiteness and brightness everywhere. When we walked out of the airport it felt as if someone had thrown ice onto my body. Devinder noticed me shivering and said that he'd go and get the car so that I wouldn't have to go into the cold. But I said I'd be okay. I didn't want to be on my own again. Inside the car it was still cold and Devinder turned and pulled me toward him. The smell of his after-shave made me feel better. I remembered the way he used to turn the bottle on to his hand making sure it wasn't too much or too little. Then he'd slap it all over his chin with a quick short movement of his big hands. I felt my coldness lessen. Out of the car window I could see brown buildings and no sun. This wasn't the Britain I'd imagined. I heard Devinder's voice saying, 'We're just coming to our place.'

It was another of the brown streets and Devinder slowed and stopped the car in front of number 19. We got out and the air felt wet. Devinder turned to look at me, his face in this damp disinfectant close felt like an echo. Inside, I stood in the hall not knowing what to do. I missed them a lot. Devinder came toward me, the smell of his leather jacket close, I turned and looked at his wide brown eyes. I tried to hide my questions and disappointment. He pulled me toward him. The dampness and stillness around was forgotten.

I remember waking up and panicking that someone might walk in and see us and then I curled up next to him enjoying the warmth of skin next to naked skin. I could lie like this all day, no one was going to interrupt us. No three year old nieces were going to barge in shouting aunty, aunty come and play with my doll or unexpected neighbours searching to seek out the new groom. Moments of privacy and bliss. I lazily moved away from him and got up, the coldness coming to my feet through the carpet and put on my salwaar and kameez. I went into the kitchen and found a pot to make some tea. The sound of icy water bashing against the pot felt loud, almost like something that shouldn't be there. I looked out of the window onto the tenements across the road while the tea boiled. When it was ready, I poured two cups and took them to the bedroom. He was still asleep. I went back into the kitchen and covered his tea with a saucer and drank my own sitting at the glass table.

The telephone rang and brought with it my future life in Britain. I could hear the loud voice at the other end. Javed had to rush off to Pakistan, his mother was seriously ill and they were short staffed.

The next day the steam from the pot and the frying onions made the kitchen hot and noisy. I stirred the pot, checked the lentils and then started the dough. Devinder came in hair dripping wet from his shower and got the plates out noisily, he was in a hurry. I was trying my best. The chappatis ballooned up into perfect balls and I slipped them off the girdle trying not to burn my fingers and placed them on Devinder's plate. His hands neatly broke a piece of chappati and folded it to make a hollow in the middle to scoop up the dahl. I could have just stood there and watched the fast hungry movements. I put on some tea. He wouldn't be back from the restaurant till late, he'd said that it depended on when the customers decided to leave. Sometimes there'd be drunks who did it just to annoy them. Devinder said that now that they didn't rule India anymore, they wanted to pretend they did, but they had to pay for it. He gulped down his tea and went into the hall. I followed him. He was sitting on a chair leaning down to his feet, tying his laces. Soon he'd be out that door and belonging to another

world. He stood up, turned suddenly to face me and gave my
arms a squeeze. 'Don't worry, I'll be back as soon as I can.'

I tried to give him a smile saying that I'd be okay.

Back in the kitchen, plates and cups stuck out of the sink,
the griddle black and abandoned lay on the cooker. It seemed
strange to think that only five minutes ago spoons and cups
clinked together. Now all lay in stillness. I dragged a chair out
from beneath the table to sit and stare. For the first time in my
life I was so alone, not even a sound around me. Something
screamed silently inside me. The whiteness of the airport, the
wind on my legs, tears, my sister crying, Asha holding on tightly
to my fingers, mum saying Beti write to us, dad standing back,
his jaw bone sinking low, making his face seem even thinner
than usual. It all seemed so long ago, so far away. I could hear
the cars and lorries outside. Slowly, I got off my chair and went
to the sink. The soap suds felt warm and nice on my hands.
Then I took the tava[6] and zig-zagged the scouring brush
against the rough shape of the cast iron, the noise filling the
kitchen and my head. When I ran water over it, the black
specks of stuck-on charcoal came away, mixing with the clear
water. The tava felt smooth and perfect by the time I had finished with it. I turned off the tap, the water stopped and again
I was alone.

It was late now. Empty, blackness, a man walking a dog.
Nothing was on television, at least nothing that interested me,
just someone talking too loud about prizes to be won.

I must have fallen asleep because I didn't hear Devinder
come in. He helped me up from the sofa and took me to the
bed. I cuddled next to him and slept nicely.

I know he has to work but for me his going to work is like a
pole being shoved through my chest slowly. The days go from
one to another in this way and I try and keep myself busy. But
how many times can you polish a table? I've started going out.
At first I'd thought that people would stare, but they look at
me and turn away. Once a man did stare hard at me and spat
on the ground. My heart thumped and I felt dirty and was glad
to get home and be in my kitchen. I sat at the table and took
out the doughnut I'd bought. The sugar stuck to my fingers and
the softness of the cake sent shivers around my mouth. My
head felt comforted by the soft buttery sponge. The woman in

the cake shop knows me now, she never says anything, just twenty-seven pence and thank you. I eat doughnuts, pastries and eiffel towers, pink jam and coconut sticking to my teeth and the sides of my mouth. Sometimes I forget the children playing in the gali[7], the shine on my niece's face, my family. My clothes have needed to be un-picked and re-sewn to give my body more space. Meanwhile I wait for something to happen and I don't look at anyone when I go out.

Glossary

1. Jija-ji   Brother-in-law
2. Bhabi-ji   Sister-in-law
3. taba   small eating house
4. betia   daughters (term used to show affection)
5. milk badaam   creamy drink made with nuts
6. tava   cast iron griddle used to cook chappatis
7. gali   street

C. Rogerson

THE WORLD AND THINGS IN IT

When people say how are you, what have you been doing, I always say oh, you know, the same old things. Not much. I can never think of anything specific or special enough to mention. But my life is full of little happenings, and every day holds newness and minor miracles and tragedies. Really, every single day. I have never had a typical day in my life. And this day was no exception.

Sarah and Tim had come for dinner, with their children, for the first time. I only knew them because our kids were friends of their kids and on impulse the previous week, maybe to atone for the fact I was late once again picking up my kids, I'd invited them for dinner.

They'd only been in the house ten minutes – my husband Robbie had nervously poured them wine, while the kids, less shy, all raced upstairs to embark on an evening of no parental shouting – when there was a knock on the door, and there stood John, holding both my cockerels upside down, with a sweaty and proud smile on his face.

'Here, hold one of these please while I do the other one in,' he politely asked me.

I had asked him to come and kill a few of the birds, but that had been weeks ago, and it took a few seconds for it all to make sense. The timing was not good. But then when is a good time to kill cockerels?

'Great, John. Which one do you want me to hold?'

'Why don't you take the white one, this red one's so vicious, it's already scratching my arm. I just saw them roosting on your bench as I walked up so I thought it would be best to grab them both at the same time.'

'Yeah, you did good John, I couldn't have done it. Especially the red one. Mean old thing, he's scratched my legs twice. Through jeans.'

John handed me the white cockerel, which was huge and heavy and not struggling at all, but hanging limp and perhaps frightened but more likely beyond fear, having been swooped up by something so much more powerful than himself. He was probably saying to himself this is not happening, and imagining himself out in the field in the corn with all the hens gossiping around him. His legs were cold and horrible to touch and his stirrup claw was deadly. Like a lot of things that are lovely to look at, up close it was quite different. His red comb looked obscene and his eyes stupid and mean.

I stood there frozen, gripping this bird, with my mere acquaintance guests inside drinking wine with my shy husband and my dinner hopefully simmering nicely, and watched John back away with the red bird.

'Bye bye red cockerel, it's been a nice year, but it couldn't last,' I mumbled inanely.

'Oh, I've said a prayer and thanked it for its life,' assured John calmly, reminding me he was no ordinary country poultry killer, but an upper class new age country poultry killer. I mentally mixed him with the dinner guests and winced. They wore matching Shetland jumpers and ironed jeans, while he had a weakness for expensive pre-fifties' clothes and earrings. Never mind, I couldn't be bothered worrying about all that social stuff. I looked away as John made a twisting and jerking movement with his arms and the red cockerel made one last squawk. That startled my cockerel into action again and it frightened me by struggling and I said,

'Quick, John, I'm going to let go.'

Ever chivalrous, he immediately let go the red one, which did not act in the least dead, and came and took the white one from me.

For no reason at all, I was reminded of the doctor's office, and the exam and the expressions on the doctor's face. Sympathy and concern only barely veiling triumph at having made a diagnosis. Probably his life was full of patients with nothing tangible wrong with them and the effort of pretending he sensed disease was exhausting and not at all why he'd wanted to become a doctor.

'Look John, it's not dead.'

'Sure it is, it's flapping about a bit, that's all. I'll go find it and put it in the boot in a minute. First do this bird, though.'

'John, maybe we should keep this one,' an idea which was new to me. Who was doing the talking here, I wondered, but suddenly it did not seem imperative to kill off both birds. 'Yeah, what do you think? This one hasn't flown up at anybody. Maybe he won't be a nuisance at all.'

'Are you sure? Now's the time, if you want to do it.'

'Nope. Let's not do it. White bird, your life has been spared.'

With that, John released the white cockerel, who flew off to join the white hen that had been perching with him when John arrived. They both perched on the gooseberry bush and fluffed their feathers and stayed perfectly still, maybe hoping by doing so that John would think they were part of the gooseberry bush and leave them in peace.

I brought John into the house, pulled off his great camel hair coat and trilby hat and generally made a fuss of him. I insisted he have dinner with us, though not much insistence was necessary. As a newly single man, he was apt to turn up at people's houses around dinner time. No matter, he was a gracious and entertaining guest.

Some of the kids' screams sounded a little serious, so after stirring the soup, I went upstairs to see them. Briefly alone, I automatically checked it – my lump – and it was still there of course, even through my jumper. A hard bit of an otherwise perfectly soft breast. A wee bit sore where they stuck the needle in for the biopsy, but no real pain. Results in three weeks. Well what's three weeks? Twenty-one days of imagining the world without me in it. Tiny waves of self pity and occasional splashes of panic eroding my days. I told no one but my husband, who seemed not to have heard, so blank was his response, and I was sort of holding my breath for three weeks and inviting near strangers for dinner to keep me on my toes.

I sorted out the squabbling, which was, needless to say, only from my lot, and returned to serve up the dinner. It went okay, the rest of that evening. The loaf I'd put out was a little dry and the pie crust was too heavy, but the ham was fine and the wine got finished and by some miracle of social symbiosis, John did not alienate my other guests and everybody pulled out fiddles and guitars and those funny round drums and stayed late enough for me to feel they weren't just being polite.

I went to bed thinking well, that's another day done, and glad it was over.

I'd been in bed when I first noticed the lump. A person of extremes, I went straight from feeling immortal to feeling on the edge of certain death. Before I even made the doctor appointment I had Robbie remarried to a younger woman and my kids not recognising old photos of me. I had the world turning on its axis without me on it. It floored me, realising how little altered the world would be. But I kept my doom to myself, in a little cold dark room with just space for me, and I only entered it once or twice a day.

The white hen went missing after that. Peculiar, because hens do not go missing, unless they've been eaten, and we've never had trouble from foxes or pine martens or dogs before. Hens do not run or fly away. They go round and round the same routes every day, no matter what. I got three new hens and the white cockerel lorded over them and continued to not act aggressive with me or the kids, maybe knowing he was on borrowed time.

The new friends invited us round for dinner and that was fine. One day the lump felt bigger, and it seemed smaller than ever the following day. I shopped, cooked, washed, cleaned, even managed to read stories to my kids, but not to myself. I was too busy chattering away to myself up there to listen to any story.

'Heard anything yet?' asked Robbie one day, so I guess he had heard me when I'd told him.

'No, not yet.'

'Well, no news is good news.' He was always a one for relying heavily on clichés to get words out, was my Robbie. And it was not lost on me that he was looking at me slightly differently lately either. A touch fearfully, if you ask me. He probably has his own room in his head too.

Then one day Gus, our youngest, came running in – I watched him run from the kitchen window and saw his face, urgent and excited – and he shouted,

'I found her, I found the white hen!'

'Alive?' I asked, doubting it.

'Yes! She's in the back shed, sitting on a hundred eggs, way below the hay bales.'

We all had to go out and see for ourselves. We'd never had a hen go broody before, oddly enough, and had given up hope. Sure enough, there she was, almost invisible in the shadows, and when we disturbed her, we could see the five tiny bantam eggs under her. We whispered good luck to her and tip-toed outside. Chicks on the horizon! It was something to look forward to.

It was funny her going broody the day after the red cockerel snuffed it. He'd always been a feisty bird – his first crow was long before we could even tell he was a cockerel, not a hen. He was just this brown ball of speckled fluff, flying up on a fence and pushing out his wee chest and making an adolescent creaky croaky sound. Letting the world know it was time to get up or time to go to bed or time to just do something for the hell of it because he said so. We all used to laugh when he strutted around, all self-important and cocky. His feathers grew in bright red and although he never got very big, the hens all knew he was boss and even I started walking around him instead of over him. The big white cockerel never even competed for the brood and had become a loner.

And now it was as if even his genes were cocky and determined to survive even if he didn't. Because we had no doubt the chicks would be his and there would probably be one or two red feathered cockerels among them.

More days passed and I began to think of them as days when I was still in the world. It began to snow, soft huge flakes that quickly quilted everything. We brought the white hen food and water. Although we never saw her eat or drink, it was always gone when we checked the next day.

Kamaljit Sangha

STRAIGHT TO THE HEART

The long tow of his breath fogs the cool surface of the mirror. It conceals the boy's reflection reminding him of his mother's youth in purdah.

Sunlight slanting through a small gap between drawn curtains cuts diagonally across his back. A dislocated curtain peg hangs off the rail. He will have to fix it before his father sees it.

The boy steps back from the mirror to see more of his reflection. He studies the scar above his right eye, proud and defiant of its sickle shape, the way it curves through his eyebrow and furrows down to the side of his head. It is a memorial to his beautiful young brother, slain in the hushed potency of puberty, banished to a clearing where the dead talk in subdued tones, spooling their voices around the present tense.

The boy resumes his shadowplay, ducking and weaving, leading with his left, harbouring his natural southpaw as the sucker punch. Occasionally he will halt a punch mid-air before its completed trajectory, freeze it, and move around to face his fist to see where on the mirror it might land. Restraint is crucial. He has known boys/men who go into an opponent all blood and thunder – mashed up anger – and lose sight of their target, expending energy throwing wasted punches.

Never let ye hands dictate ye mind, make sure ye see his fist comin early. You watch football, right? It's like a goalie watchin a player's body shape just before he strikes a penalty. Always watch the birdie.

The boy wonders if the advice of a local boxing coach is self-evidently true. Would his brother be still alive if he had taken it?

The boy drops his hands to his sides and steps away from the mirror, the pain beneath his scar a needle pushing through throbbing skin. He paces slowly around the bed relaxing his shoulders and neck muscles. Sometimes adrenaline flows over every ridge of his brain and he wonders what it must be like to dive off a high cliff or walk a tightrope between two high rise buildings in order to save someone's life.

After training in front of the mirror the boy tries to balance the blood rolling inside his head. He thinks about a film in which a character sits cross-legged on the floor and tries to balance blue water in a tank he keeps in his house, staring intensely until vision is blurred and the beholder is part of the flowing liquid. Sometimes the boy watches the film on a video tape he hides under his wardrobe, staring at the actor concentrating on the tank until the boy's vision, too, becomes blurred.

The boy looks at the photograph on his bookcase, a crumpled polaroid taken just before the '79 Cup Final. He, his brother and their father, are crouched like footballers in the bottom row of a squad photo, the boys either side of their father, his thick arms wrapped around their shoulders, steadying all three. The boy remembers how they celebrated an important United victory: his father dancing around the living room balancing a glass of rum on top of his head, telling the boy to turn up the volume on the stereo, while his brother, Kiran, applauded and followed his father's meandering footsteps ready to catch the glass in case it fell. The boys' mother would come in and lean against the door and laugh at them pretending to be famous footballers, calling her husband show-off when he tried to back heel a ball of paper. Before he leaves he pulls her away from the door and serenades her around the room, whispering in her ear as she lifts the moving glass off his head, the boys clapping hard and fast to the rhythm of the music, safe in the knowledge that everyone was happy and having a good time.

The boy puts down the photo. Sometimes he wonders why he keeps it there, as it is. Why he doesn't just have one of him and his brother in the light of him and his father's sour relationship: a man who ignores his only living child's birthday and believes he is the murderers' accomplice: so-called hero who took them on because he wanted to test the big brother big man theory when it would have been easier to make a run for it.

No, he would leave it on the bookcase, in case someone wanted positive proof of the once good relationship between the man and his two boys, and mother who took a photograph for the first time in her life.

The boy unravels the tape on his knuckles and puts it under his mattress. He takes off his sweat-drenched t-shirt and uses it to wipe the condensation off the mirror, repeating the motion clockwise to make double sure. The boy's father constantly searches his room to find something to use against him: cigarettes, condoms, a letter of reprimand from the boy's headmaster. Anything to eliminate the boy's child status: hoist him to the point where he will never forget the look on his father's blood-filled face and make him see life from the height of a ruined man.

On Saturdays the boy's father will barge in with a hoover into his room as the postman shuts the gate. The boy will pretend to sleep. He will not stir until he hears the sound of the machine begin to fade and the curved flex disappear under the door. Then, when he is ready to go back to sleep, all soft and warm, his father returns with a bucket of water and chamois to clean the window. The boy's patience gives way and he clambers slowly out of bed, turning slightly to watch his father standing on a stool, vigorously cleaning, right up to the window. Close enough to fall through it.

The boy's mother calls him to sweep up the leaves in the garden. He tells her he is on his way. He takes out a tracksuit and changes quickly. As he closes his door he looks across at the door to his brother's room. He opens it and steps inside.

The football posters have been replaced by ones of religious icons, their exaggerated portraits turning the room into a shrine. On a bed-side cabinet his mother has started to collect alms. The figures on the posters follow the boy around the room: set halos and finely-made clothes, portraits mocking the struggles of a faith born out of a wish to end false images.

The boy turns to the remaining blank wall, scarred by former posters. He runs his hands up and down its surface, occasionally sweeping them in an arc, acting out a prepared method of atonement. He presses his back against the wall and lets out a gasp, as if he has sipped on something too strong. He comes off the wall and settles down on the edge of the bed and stares at the floor. The toe of a training shoe juts out from under the bed. He picks it up to study its contours, encouraging him to remember why his brother always put in a layer of cleaning sponge. Kiran said it was to get more speed off the mark just in case of trouble. He drops the shoe and it turns over on its side as he kicks it back under the bed. He recalls his brother wearing black leather shoes on the day he was murdered, always complaining they pinched the knuckle of his toes and scraped up bits of skin, making him stop in his tracks and curse the manufacturers where he worked every Saturday.

The boy lowers his head into his cuffed hands. He tugs his hair and slaps the sides of his head, hot tears roll down his face. A car decelerates outside the house. He gets up off the bed, wiping his face, and walks over to the window and watches his mother's employer get out of the car. He goes back to the bed and straightens the eiderdown, listening to the conversation in the hallway. Part of it is wedged against the wall. He bends over and tugs at it and loses his balance and falls on to the bed. He lies there, face smudged in the print of the cover, waiting for his brother's heart to beat again.

Every night the boy dreams his brother's death and the ensuing events. A long, silent, blade; crying relatives hovering over a body in a sunlit kitchen; footballers with black hoods wearing death masks; swastikas and pig's blood. A chain of welded symbols pressing against his flesh, tormenting his young body and turning him over like a carcass cooking over a fire.

The boy washes his face and goes downstairs. From the open kitchen door he watches his mother prepare samosas, pulling chunks off a large ball of dough, rolling one and stretching it until it is shaped into a triangle to hold the accompanying vegetables, before it is deep fried. She turns around to face him and, without speaking, lifts her head and points him in the direction of the garden. He wonders why she doesn't say to him, I love you, anymore. As he walks passed her he wishes he could put his arms around her waist and rest his head in the cool hollow of her back. Mum. Mum. Please.

Everyday at work the boy's father imagines his son and wife hanging on to each other, conspiring against him in his absence.

Since his brother's death neither of the boy's parents touch him. He feels he lives in a quarantined environment, and that they look at him through a glass partition trying to decide what to do. When he goes to the supermarket he feels like one of the bar-coded items swept through the electronic system and stuffed into a plastic bag.

The boy steps out into the garden and goes to the shed to fetch a rake. Clouds brood overhead as if in the first phase of amok. He recently read in a story the three phases – brooding, frenzy, amnesia – which give rise to it. He wonders if the leaves on the grass are victims of amok, ravaged by ruthless gusts, or plucked by a foreign hand from their place of origin. He looks at the balding tree next to the east-facing fence and then back down the leaves, victim to nature's timeless holocausts: stateless brown leaves, bereft of branch and tree, waiting to be piled up and carted away.

The boy rakes to the smell of frying samosas. He thinks they are his wages. He leans on the handle of the rake and gazes west, thinking the second batch always taste better than the first because they are cooked at the right temperature, and then, before they are ready to eat, dipped and pulled through a combination of chutney and ketchup, bite into the crisp, protective exterior then soft, mushy vegetables. A chilled glass of fizzy on the side.

The boy continues raking the leaves, occasionally looking up to see his mother standing at the cooker. He remembers the day he thought he was his mother's favourite – eleven years old, walking through the schoolyard, playing with the coin in his pocket, turning it over and slipping it through his fingers feeling the insignia graze against them. A boy walks up to him and says, Some paki woman got spat on by a loada fifth formers in the high road.

That morning the boy's mother had told him she would be shopping in the high road near his school. During his last lesson the boy imagines her walking away from her assailants, oblivious to the bile snailing down the back of her coat. People behind her on the bus whisper, A you gonna tell 'er or shall I? Naw, leave it. Black bastards.

After the last bell the boy leaps from his chair and sprints for home, dodging the other children as they drag their feet to the main exit, his arms flailing, farting anxiously, tongue bitten several times as he swallows all the oxygen he can, running full tilt around every corner, the weight of his bag throwing him close to the kerb, down the high street – 'Watch it son!' – and through the rec', mud flying up the back of his trousers, finally swerving into his road, eyes gurgling in their sockets, blood swilling inside his head, 75, 77, 79, 81, 83... Up and over the low front wall – his knee catching a loose brick and tearing his trousers – and into the porch, searching for the key in the lining of his jacket, hot sweat rolling like wood shavings down the sides of his face as he finds the key and jams it into the lock upsidedown then rightwayup, blood and shit mixing inside him, the twisted strap of the bag cutting into his neck, and then, just as it reaches a crescendo too much for a boy to bear, his mother, right there in front of him with her hand on the open door, good and proper in spite of some flour on the tip of her nose, stepping back sharply to cushion his head as he rushes into her midriff, her hand coming off the door and pushing it through his hair, leaving a white streak of flour down the middle, listening to him sobbing.

Mum! Mum!... Everything's gonna be alright.

Every day the boy's father rises at five am; shaves, washes, dresses and eats alone. He has the dial on the radio on the same frequency all the time. If someone moves it without his consent and forgets to put it back where it belongs it will be assumed they are trying to cause unnecessary conflict. His wife is not allowed to rise until her husband leaves the house. He does not want a woman near him before he arrives at work to supervise the women who he claims torture him all day long. Occasionally an early morning overseas telephone call disturbs his routine and for a short time what is left of them as a family crowd around the telephone to speak to the caller.

Before she goes to bed at night the boy's mother prepares her husband's lunch for the following day and puts it in the fridge to keep their lives as cool as possible.

Time is running out before the boy's father gets home from work. He rakes briskly to the sound of the wind penetrating his clothes. He takes off his tracksuit top to let the wind purge and chasten his anger. He wonders if it's strong enough to pick and scoop him up over the chimney stacks, taking him high above the world's surface to a place where he will no longer be dragged through the mire of adult contempt. He turns toward the house and sees his mother gesturing him to get on with it.

The boy bends down and rakes harder and faster, gathering the leaves in several piles. They are as good as cleared. He checks the time. His father will be home in half an hour. He walks around the garden picking up strays. A gust of wind brings down more from a neighbour's oak. He runs towards them as they swirl about, pirouetting, making mock dives, shouting the name of the United goalkeeper. Enjoying himself. Having fun.

He stops, feeling embarrassed. A little girl stands at a neighbour's window, pointing and laughing. He straightens up and beckons her to come out. She points her index finger up to the sky as if to say, It's too cold, mummy won't let me out. He waves at her and she disappears behind the curtain. He waves at her again after he fetches a bin liner from the shed. This time the little girl waves back, her hand flapping so furiously it becomes a part of speech. He puts his lips to his hand and blows her a kiss. The little girl puts a finger up her nose and blows one back. The boy laughs as he ties a knot at the top of the bag and rests it against the conservatory wall.

He takes off his trainers and wallops the soles against each other. Drops of rain begin to fall. He bends down and picks up a twig from the earth and works at getting the dirt out of the patterns of the soles. He thinks about his mock exams in a month's time and knows if he doesn't do well his parents will be on his back again. Kiran always wanted to go to university. He would tell his brother he was going to be a lawyer – all the trimmings: office, secretary, nice flat. The works. Everything just waiting for him, as if it was a poem he carried around inside himself and one day would surely transcribe.

The boy is not allowed to stay up after 9.30pm, so he uses a small torch and reads under the covers. Music must not be played louder than the low volume setting on the television, no posters on his bedroom walls and no going out after school unless it is specifically authorised.

At school, when his friends ask him about a comedy programme screened the previous night, the boy nods his head and waits for them to divulge the story line before he chips in with his own comments. *What about that bit when he...* And he nods and synchronises his laughter accordingly.

He wonders what his schoolfriends would make of such a shameless idea of home.

The boy closes the conservatory doors and shoots the bolt upright. He goes back into the house and sees his mother standing at the sink washing flour off her arms and hands. The sight of her doing this makes him hungry, the smell of cooked samosas filling his nostrils. He smiles at his mother. She asks if he has finished. He nods, imitating her at the sink. She sees him mocking her and lets out a gentle, soul-stirring laugh, long enough to catch them in a shared light. He washes and dries his hands as his mother takes a plate out of the cupboard next to the cooker and puts on it half a dozen freshly-made samosas. He dives into a bottom cupboard and pulls out a bottle of ketchup. He puts it on the table and notices a dried, red crust has formed under the lid. It reminds him of the congealed blood on his hands on the day of his brother's murder. *Not now. Don't.*

He sits and eats alone. His mother takes out a tub of chutney from the fridge and places it in front of him. Two bangles on her wrist collide as she pulls her arm away. He shuts his eyes. She turns and goes to another part of the house.

The samosas taste as good as ever. They remind the boy of the kind of pleasure he used to share about dal with his grandfather. The boy had loved his ancestor more than anyone else. He made the boy feel part of an important chain of events running the course of the century. There were gifts, jokes, stories; sips of army rum and two generations on a bicycle silhouetted by the setting sun. All wrapped in unconditional love.

One central Punjab morning his grandfather came into his room and gently woke him, upright finger on his lips as the boy rubbed his eyes and asked him the time. Dawn was breaking and the boy could smell drifting woodsmoke through the wire-meshed kitchen window where his grandmother was making tea. The boy gasped as his grandfather lifted his head and put a gold chain around the boy's neck. Then the old man kissed his grandson on the forehead and told him to go back to sleep. The boy stays awake, twirling the chain and feel it slither around his neck, his young heart full of happiness and joy.

The boy's mother returns to clear his plate. She asks him what he thinks of the samosas. Before he can reply the phone rings. His father asks the boy's mother if she needs anything from the shop. The boy hears her say eggs and yes, as if she is answering a question about the leaves. The boy continues chewing, rapidly losing his appetite. He grabs the last samosa while his mother is still on the phone, gags his mouth with it and goes into the shower room to stare at his reflection. He stands there nodding at each thought entering his head, mixing up loneliness, wet dreams, revenge, half a samosa sticking out while the rest of it crumbles quietly in his mouth. Feeling sick, he takes out the remainder and throws it into the bin. He looks at the bottle of ketchup on the table and grabs it by the throat and takes it to the sink and runs the tap. His hands start to shake as he finishes squeezing out the sauce. He hears his mother hang up and make a call. A gust blows as he opens the conservatory doors and makes him fall back on his heels. He wonders if he should bury it in the earth or hurl it across several gardens. He thinks about the little girl watching from the nearby house and decides to squash the bottle into the bag of leaves. He pushes it into the middle, touches its stomach where the bottle shows a slight bulge, and reties the bag.

The boy's mother stands at the sink drying dishes. She raises her head and asks him what he was doing. I heard a funny noise. It was the wind – conservatory door was banging. I didn't shut it properly.

The boy tells his mother he is going to his room to finish

homework. She nods and he walks out of the kitchen and trudges upstairs. Before he reaches his room he hears his mother shouting his name, repeating the word leaves. The boy rushes back downstairs wondering what all the fuss is about. The shouting gets louder. He jumps the last three steps and twists his ankle as he lands. He sits up rubbing his injured foot. His mother's shouts increase. He slowly gets up and hobbles into the kitchen clutching his thigh. He sees his mother rush out into the garden. He stoops and drags himself to the conservatory, the samosas churning in his gut.

The leaves have burst through the bag and swirl around the mother's head. The wind loosens her hair, free and wild. The rain belts down and plasters her face. She pleads him to come out, an outstretched hand begging for help. He shudders at the sight of her and wants to bolt the doors and leave her to her fate, pack a bag and run away. He beckons her to come back inside. She picks up the empty ketchup bottle and waves it like a tomahawk. Over his shoulder he hears the front door open and shut. The boy looks at his watch. Footsteps engulf the hallway. The boy's heart rises to his throat.

A tongue of fire is about to extinguish the rain.

Hamid Shami

NEW MAN

Bought
blue
contact lenses,
Bleached
my hair
blonde,
Even changed
my name,
It is now Charlie.

Still they call me
Paki.

ASK A PAKISTANI

There's the expert
What Indian restaurant
Would you recommend?

None –
They're all shite.

But seriously?

Seriously –

Iain Crichton Smith

THE GAME

We were playing football with a fishing cork, Daial and myself, on a full-sized football pitch. We were both wearing shirts; mine was green, his was blue. He looked very thin. Of course, he had been ill and some said it was TB: everyone was frightened of TB.

What a beautiful summer's day it was. No smoke rose from the chimneys for no fires were required. We played in silence for the pitch was a big one, and very demanding. Also the cork screwed sideways when you hit it with your shoe. Normally in summer we didn't wear shoes but we couldn't play 'football' without them.

Neither of us was winning: in fact, no goals at all had been scored. This was our favourite pastime and we had many heroes among the adult footballers, including Stoodie and Hoddan. One was a centre-forward, the other a centre-half: both strongly-built and adventurous. Maybe some day we would play for the district too.

A good distance away from the pitch, Strang passed with his dog. He didn't notice us: he always strode forward in a great hurry. Tall and red-faced, he was one of the healthiest among us and we couldn't work out why he wasn't in the war. We liked his collie dog Patch very much.

I must be getting better, I thought, I'm not sweating as much as usual. Daial wasn't sweating so much either. It was wonderful to be out in the fresh air: as we ran we felt it streaming around our necks. I dribbled past Daial but lost the cork at the corner flag. We were really very poor; we used to have a proper ball but since it burst, we couldn't afford another one. Indeed, I don't know who was the poorer, Daial or myself. Though our poverty didn't usually bother us, except when we couldn't afford a ball.

The cork was of course one that would normally be found attached to a fishing net. When he grew up Daial was going to be a fisherman: I didn't want to be one. I was more ambitious, I wanted to go to university or college though it was hard to see how I could afford to do that unless I won a bursary.

At half-time we lay on our backs gazing up at the white clouds. I was quire tired though pleasantly so. I nibbled a blade of grass at the side of the pitch. In the distance I could hear Strang shouting to his dog; also I could see Maggie hanging out her washing: her legs were very red and fat. I wondered what Janet would be doing. Once, playing draughts with her father and she sitting between us, I placed my hand on her thigh under the table: she didn't move a muscle. What an extraordinary sensation that was.

We rose to our feet at the end of ten minutes or what we thought was ten minutes for neither of us had a watch. Some day I might have a watch but not yet. Janet had a thin gold watch which her father had given her but he owned the village shop. I thought I heard my mother's voice calling me but that must have been an error for I didn't see her about the house. She didn't like me playing football in case I became ill again. I was often ill with bronchitis: TB however was more dangerous and my father had died of it. He used to give me rides on his shoulders and at one time he would smoke a pipe. He was also less strict than my mother.

As I dribbled past Daial I was looking straight at the sea and what seemed to be a becalmed ship. All day, though often we were not aware of it, there was the sound of the sea. Indeed, one of my favourite Gaelic poems was entitled in English, The High Swelling of the Sea. It was about an exile who wanted to be buried beside the sea; it was a sad, beautiful song.

Looking at the sea I had forgotten about the cork and now Daial was in a good position to score. A few months ago we had gathered scrap iron for the War Effort. We had found an old wreck of a car which we were pretending to drive; there were hardly any cars in the village.

Daial screwed the cork past the post so it was still nil–nil. Since this was wartime, we could see many ships passing and wondered whether any of the village boys was on any of them. Daial had two brothers in the Navy: I had one. The last we heard from him he was in New York. The money he sent my mother arrived late, and this caused us problems, for we were absolutely dependent on it. I couldn't imagine New York at all: our only town, Stornoway, was large enough for me. Whenever I thought of Stornoway I felt the intensely cold ice cream on my teeth, or I smelt apples. Red apples nesting among straw; though I hadn't seen many recently. I hadn't seen many oranges either, or sweets. Once I had eaten whale meat but didn't like it.

I could hear the barking of a dog: Strang must be coming

back. And what was very strange, he was crossing the pitch. I shouted at him because he was coming between me and the 'ball'. His face looked very red and healthy and smooth-shaven. He didn't see me at all nor did he see the 'ball' though it was at his feet. He strode forward relentlessly towards the smokeless village.

Ian Stephen

PIKE

The pier at Gartmorn Dam had standing-room for three anglers. A steel cylinder was linked to the concrete bank by a walkway. It must have been placed there to monitor the supply, or pump it, when this reservoir had served the area. Like everything else in a radius of Alloa, rust had shoved the galvanising aside. You reached onto the pier by stepping round a locked gate and going out onto a lattice of metal.

It was sided by pines. Probably planted in a post-war panic, anticipating the future demand for pit-props and wood pulp. These had fared well and now kept most winds off the water. So there was normally the reflection of a real island, forested and about half a mile out. The picture in the water was something to look at, set in an algae soup of insects. That's probably why bigger fish also gathered around the pier. They would chase the sticklebacks and perch-fry that chased the insects.

You could catch the first dimples of disturbance. Could be just a breeze escaping through branches – until you saw fry break surface. Maybe you'd catch the metal glint of an accelerating fish below. I leaned out to watch all this and could have been looking at mackerel chasing sandeels.

I'd spend my paper-round money between the blue painted Sports Shop and the Co-Op fish shop across the road. Wire traces with treble hooks didn't come cheap, even if the white-haired lady knocked a penny or two off. She'd ask me to keep on talking, just so she could hear the accent and say my curls were wasted on a boy. And herring fillets came from the Clyde or Canada, so clean that they didn't smell of fish. Could maybe have been trawled from the chlorine waters, inside the sandstone Public Baths, the other side of the junction.

It must have been New Year's Day because I hadn't any papers to deliver. It might have been the first day of the seventies. I was stocked-up with gear, between Christmas and Hogmanay tips. These came from the first few parts of my round, up from Main Street and still all Council territory. Further up the hill, there were too many people like us. Refugees from Council schemes in other parts of Scotland and now saddled with mortgages they couldn't afford for a bungalow with at least one dormer window or porch to make it different from next door. The real money was another grade up the hill. Some of them got The Times and there was a lot of Scotsmans to The Record.

I now lived in a reservoir. And fished the wet one, in the winter, except on the few days there was a thin coating of ice. I cast a herring-fillet from the narrow walkway and paid out line, going round the spikes to take me back to the concrete. Big guys arrived on bikes with drop-handlebars. They normally went after salmon but even on the Tay there was a couple of months closed. They had Barbour jackets and gaffs. They had reels with numbered grades of tension, worked from the back. They told me to wait for a run. Don't hit him till he's turned.

Like conger, I asked. Like conger, they agreed.

While one of them played a fish, not much bend in his rod because all his line was running out as he fiddled with the drag, I watched my nylon go out the three feet they said it would. I waited then struck and it worked. At first it was a weight then it came in with me. I wound fast and it slashed at the surface. I remembered to give line like the books said, then, next time it surfaced, I just held on. The rod was jerking. Then I was winding, pulling it by its wide open mouth, a treble hook visible in a jaw. The teeth were prominent, like those of a conger or ling, but the marblings, the camouflage, were shades of reed and water-lily. A strange tangle of light, bright enough to be shocking, rising from that thick water. It was three and a quarter pounds on their spring-balance. Do you want to put it back, they asked. I shook my head.

Well, some of these Polish guys will take one from you. A lot of them had been airmen who got stranded here at the end of the war. Or met local women. There was a back-street shop in Alloa where you could buy salami and stuff. But I brought it home. My mother made an effort. She didn't know why the book said it was an ugly fish. Mrs Beeton was of the opinion they were good-eating but inclined to be dry and so required plenty of basting. We forked at the baked fish but no-one really liked it.

Most days I caught none but once I caught four, all of them smaller than the first one. When my mother said I shouldn't have taken them home and my sister said it was cruel to kill fish, I said I knew someone who would take them. One of the names on one of the morning papers was foreign enough to be someone who would eat pike. I never knocked on that door.

I buried them to make maggots. I'd read this in one of the angling books from the main library. When I dug-up the rotted and softened flesh, some weeks later, it had worked. The skulls and teeth and shrunken eyes were recognisable. That resilient skin still showed a smudged print of the pattern. The maggots which moved incessantly, in between everything, were smaller than the ones you bought in the tackle shop. I couldn't get the smell from my hands.

One Sunday we went through to Glasgow. My father had managed to get the car tested and taxed. He waxed it like the others in the street. I remember his waypoints: Dobies' Loan; Great Western Road; Kersland Street. This was an aunt-by-marriage, on my mother's side.

She said she smiled at those who, by way of condolence, said, so she was still in Glasgow. She loved it, here. We had all to come with her now, on the underground. It didn't go anywhere you needed to go but she brought all her visitors this way. There was talk of doing away with it so you had to grab these chances.

She bought our tickets and we sat on leather benches, holding rails. The smell of the seats made me think of old books. The chrome was the pipework of a BSA. Our next-door neighbour, back in the cul-de-sac, back on the Island – he was always polishing. Not today he wouldn't be. And the glimmer of brass was my first pike from Gartmorn Dam.

We got out at Kelvin Bridge. This was near the Botanics. They were all ready to get back to the flat to catch up on the news and have some tea. They could walk round by a few shop windows. Didn't matter that they were shut. Better that way. Yes, I could go to the Botanics on my own. Sure I knew how to get back to the flat? Well here's the address and phone number on the card, just in case.

My landmark was a snooker-room. Smoke spilled out of the windows. A blackboard at the door said, *Private Club*. The flat was round the next corner.

I was hit by the sweaty smell of the Camellia rooms. I took in all the names, going down a gear into sleepiness. Sunday afternoons were always like that, trapped near a bar of the electric fire. My mother wouldn't let me go fishing but I don't think it was religious. Just trying to get me to think of something different to do.

Still in the Botanics, I found carp. You couldn't say they

were merely goldfish. The products of sustained programmes of breeding, specifically for settings like this, they flourished their features. One had a stark colour scheme of red and white. Another would have a dorsal fin like a sail. Pectorals on another would move like orange seaweed. These fish were big and lazy and mouthed at any items that fell into their oxygenated pools.

Bet you wouldn't mind dropping a line to one of them.

I started because of the accuracy. It was spoken in a soft tone, recognisably Glasgow but slow in pace and without the hard edges of the mining suburbs, or the Fife side.

Hold on and I'll see if they'll go for a Mint Imperial, he said. Aboot your age, we used to figure oot ways to catch wan. No tae kill it or eat it or anything, jist tae get a right look at it, like.

He'd have been about forty to fifty. Dressed like anybody else, in a jacket and good trousers. A cap but I think it was an open-necked shirt. Could have been a polo-neck. I don't remember a tie.

I found I was talking. Telling him I fished for trout and pike where I lived now. Where did I used to live, then, with that accent? No, he liked it, a change. The Hebrides. Aye, he'd guessed aboot there.

So you're a pike-fisher then. Quite far up the piscatorial pecking order an that? I liked the way he talked like the angling books. We were out of the hothouses now. I was talking again and he was gravitating towards the Kelvin. Any fish there, I asked and I wasn't too keen on his laugh.

Is it too dirty, then? I thought of the maroon colour that came on the Devon before it met the Forth. Someone else had laughed when I had asked if it was peat washed into the water after a spate. It was from Tilicoultry paper-mill, whatever shade was on offer that day.

Aye, it's dirty, he said, but they've made a start on it, cleaning up the Clyde. Talk of the first salmon for God knows how many years. And now, he said, if you wouldn't mind being lookout, I've had one lunchtime pint too many the day.

Are even the pubs open here on a Sunday, I asked.

I kent ye were a real teuchter, he said. Well, the hotel bars anyway. Here's the ideal place, if you jist keep a wee eye peeled for any old dears coming along.

It was a sort of tunnel, with the grass turfs growing over it and the path passing all the way through. It had turned dull and not many people were about. I said the coast was clear.

He carried on speaking as he was pissing, looking over his shoulder towards me. I lost the thread of what he was saying. Just hearing the tone of his voice. He turned, shaking the drops off his cock and said, no a bad size, that wan eh? Would ye no like to have one like that, yersel, eh?

Maybe my own fins were bristling then, ready to drive me out of the confined area, back to the light. But I didn't try to run or anything. I would have had about two yards start, more really because he wouldn't have been able to start running until he'd got his zip up.

I just stayed still. He said, in much the same tone, maybe a wee edge of something that wasn't there before, I suppose you're too shy now, to show me yours.

I still didn't get into gear. Just backed off.

Now I can see it, instinct serving you, just keeping it slow, getting you away from the hazard, hearing my own voice saying yes I was too shy and then getting towards the surface, out of the tunnel. Some fifty yards later, not running but walking fast, looking over the shoulder. He made no effort to come after me.

Back at the flat, over pancakes, and back in the car and back in the bungalow on Hungry Hill, I never said anything. It wasn't exactly a big debate going on in my mind but I remember considering whether to say anything. Maybe he'd be bothering someone else. Maybe it was more than bother.

Think that afternoon went right out of my mind, till one time I was back in the West End, just into the Nineties. Round at Bank Street, remembering the way to the Botanics. Within a mile or so radius of that tunnel, I saw it all again. Heard his voice. Felt my muscles quiver like fins. Looked for the open light, people swimming by.

Jean Tarras

SURVIVORS

'Shut up you little bugger,' she yelled, 'or I'll fucking well belt you.'

The child howled louder than ever and she bent down, picked him up, held him at arm's length and shook him. Blond curls bobbed on a slender neck swaying like a flower in the wind. The howls turned into great heaving sobs. Marie was suddenly frightened, hugged him to her chest and rocked him.

'Shush, shush,' she murmured. 'I'm sorry, so sorry.'

She looked little more than a child herself as she wandered about the room, chubby child wetting her T-shirt with his tears, one of his hands clasping the pleat of thick fair hair that hung over her shoulder. Her hazel eyes were tender as she soothed him.

'God, what a mess,' she thought as she looked around.

Three floors up. Worn, bleach edged curtains strung across the window. A square of beige carpet on which stood a settee, the cushions spewing their contents from the corners where little fingers had pushed and poked.

Dave's sobs became hiccups, and seating him on a thin hip she went through to the kitchen. There was a dribble of milk in the carton and she transferred it to his mug and took a biscuit from the half empty packet. Back on his feet he toddled to the sitting room. He staggered and sat down. Before he could open his mouth to cry again she closed his hands round the mug and put the biscuit beside him. Back in the kitchen she filled a pan with water and put it on the only ring of the cooker which was still working, then threw a tea bag into a mug. She leaned her elbows on the sink full of unwashed dishes and gazed out of the window onto the square of grass far below. Idly she noticed that yet another of the clothes' poles had been vandalised and lay like a felled tree. The grass was a dirty brown green. Two thin dogs raced round the corner and stopped to relieve themselves, adding their excrement to the tins and crisp packets blowing in eddies in the wind tunnel produced by the block of flats.

The water boiled and she poured it into the mug. Swirling the tea bag around she fished it out and left it to dry on the side of the sink. Sipping the pale gold liquid she opened the cupboard door. Baked beans, two eggs, a tin of soup, half a loaf. She would have to get potatoes.

Her purse was in her coat pocket. Saturday and Sunday were hell. No money till Monday. The meagre contents were spread on the work top. Just enough for potatoes and a pack of tobacco; she had enough papers.

Finishing her tea she bundled Dave into his coat, hat and gloves. He started to whinge again and she lifted her hand, then dropped it and bent to give him a kiss instead. Grabbing his buggy, she struggled down the three flights with him in her arms and the buggy bumping behind.

The supermarket was warm and light. Dave liked the movement and noise in the shop, and Marie felt her spirits rise. She put the potatoes in her basket and looked with longing at the bananas. They'd have to wait until Monday. There were bargains everywhere, she thought wryly, if you happened to have money for bargains. She saw her neighbour, Martha at the wine counter. Martha's new red rinse blazed under the lights, and Jake was hanging onto her arm. Marie wondered how long he had been back and how long he would stay this time. They were never together for more than an hour or two before they were shouting at each other. Oh God, that meant there would be the noise of quarrels and fights through the wall tonight. Though maybe that was better than the sounds from the lads' bedroom on the other side. She couldn't help it, those sort of goings on never seemed normal to her.

Dave was restored to good humour and pointed with his fat hands to the sweets at the checkout. She had just enough left for a Milky Way.

It was a chilly afternoon but she walked towards the beach. Seemed silly they lived so close to the sea and hardly ever saw it.

The tide was out so she manoeuvred the buggy down the steps onto the sand. Finding a sheltered spot she unstrapped Dave.

Milky Way clutched in a melting lump in one hand, he dug the other into the sand and let it trickle through his fingers.

Marie, head resting on her hands with the bitten finger nails, watched the monotonous ebb and flow of the waves. An oil rig sat on the horizon, unreal, a creature from another planet. She wished she had paper and pencil so that she could draw it. She'd been real good at art at school.

She glanced down at Dave now clarted with chocolate and sand and playing with a pebble. He looked up at her and grinned. He really was adorable. His fair hair was curly. That couldn't have come from her; her hair was thick and straight. He was plump and she was thin, but that was natural, he was only just starting to walk. He'd thin down as he got more active.

There was the top of an aerosol can lying nearby and picking it up she scooped the softer sand from the surface and packed the lid with damp sand. Dave crowed with delight as she turned out a miniature castle. She moved away a little and made a circle of castles. Dave crawled towards them and proceeded to demolish them one by one. Marie leaned back on her hands and gazed at the horizon once more. A single mother, she thought, hardly the most popular people these days. Well, it wasn't really her fault, it was that doctor who'd landed her in this mess. She'd gone to ask for the Pill

'No need,' he'd said. 'After your operation for ovarian cysts it is 99% certain that you won't be able to have children.'

She'd cried that night. Cried for what could never be. Then she'd gone a bit mad. Slept around, and after a year found out that the doctor's 99% might be right, the other 1% was also correct. She was pregnant.

Well, she'd had the baby. After all, it might be the only one she'd ever achieve.

In any case, because her mother and father hadn't wanted her it didn't follow that she didn't want Dave. She'd been dumped into care when she was little. That wasn't going to happen to Dave. She'd learned how to fight over the years and she'd fight for him too and teach him how to get by in this bloody awful world.

If only she wasn't so tired. If only there was some let up. Some relief from the constant struggle. Occasional new clothes instead of charity shop bargains. Even the prices there were going up.

'It's only £2,' the woman had said when she looked at a pair of jeans the other day. Who did these people think they were! They could afford to work without pay, how could they know what £2 was. If they knew they wouldn't say, 'Only £2.'

She'd shaken her head and left the shop. Jumble sales were cheaper.

It would be getting dark soon, they'd better get back. She

didn't fancy the streets in the dark, with menacing figures lurking on the corners. They'd have egg and chips for tea. Then there'd be enough potatoes left for beans and chips tomorrow and she'd manage to borrow some milk from Martha. Martha sometimes made money at the weekend and she was fond of Dave. Or if Martha was skint she'd take a walk up to Scarbrook where the rich folk lived. Sometimes they went off for the weekend, leaving their milk delivery on the doorstep. Flaming idiots some of them were.

She was glad when she reached the flats once more, her legs trembling. Why did she feel so weak? Must be because she'd only had a slice of toast today. Martha was always saying that she was too thin.

The flats looked worse than ever in the fading light. The bottom flat had been boarded up and graffiti was spray painted on the door. She kicked aside an empty can and used condoms from the bottom step and bounced Dave up the stairs. Bloody hell, how her arms ached.

Dave was asleep and she left him while she cooked the eggs and chips. Having eaten, he fell asleep again so she simply washed his face and hands, changed him into his pyjamas and packed him into his cot. His eyes opened momentarily and he smiled up at her before uttering a contented sigh and slipping back into slumber.

'I love you,' she said. 'I love you so much I could eat you.' She kissed his bulging brow and soft cheeks.

She felt better now, she thought with surprise. Amazing what a walk and egg and chips could do. Putting on a pan of water to wash the dishes she ate the cold chips which Dave had left and went to examine the electric meter. There should be enough to last until Monday if she was careful. She could go to bed early or sit in the dark, and she and Dave could go out again tomorrow if it was fine. That way there would be no need for the electric fire.

Imbued with a sudden burst of energy she washed the dishes and tidied the kitchen, washing down the work tops. It didn't look too bad now. If she could only save £8 she'd buy a tin of paint and do it over. She'd tried to put £1 a week by but somehow it never worked. Something always cropped up.

With a mug of tea made from the used tea bag she went though to the sitting room and rolled herself a cigarette. She undid her hair and let it flow over her shoulders. This was bliss, this was heaven. Curling up on the settee she indulged in day dreams.

Someday, when Dave was at school, she would get a job. She'd apply for a transfer away from here, to the country maybe. To a house with a garden; she could grow vegetables then. They said vegetables were good for children and it couldn't be too difficult growing them, thousands of people did it. Dave could go to the village school, could grow up strong and healthy. She would find a job in a shop, she thought she would like that. A fine clean job, maybe in a chemist's, surrounded by cosmetics, soap, talcs and lovely smells. She might even meet someone nice and Dave could have a dad someday.

He had one already, of course, but heaven only knew where. That was the stupid sort of question the Child Support Agency asked

'And where is his father?'

As if she could tell them where, she wasn't even sure who he was! Typical! If there were greater idiots in the world than social workers and officials of any kind she'd yet to meet them. Didn't live in the real world they didn't.

God, she'd forgotten that she had an appointment on Monday with the Social. About a cooker. Not that they'd help, they'd tell her to buy a ring for the old one despite the fact that the mice had got in and chewed the wires at the back. Or they would offer her a loan and dock her money. There's no way that she would take that, she could hardly manage as it was.

She'd tackle Jim round the corner and ask him to have a look out in the skips. You could get some good things that way.

The street light outside the window snapped into life and the room was filled with shadows. It was a bugger really, life. Not that she wasn't lucky in a way. She wasn't homeless like some she saw in the shop doorways and she had Dave. Dave was a life line, hers to love, all hers. And it was staying that way. No nosy parker of a social worker was ever going to take him away.

Life would be easier if she made money on the game and she knew it. When she looked in the mirror she realised that with some make-up she could make quite a bit down Market Street each night. She'd good neighbours when they weren't stoned out of their minds, they'd look after Dave for her if she wanted.

She'd been tempted, then she'd thought there might be a

fire while she was out, or a fight and the police would be called. Where would Dave be then? In care, that's where, as fast as you could say it. It wasn't worth the risk. She'd wait until he was at school and then get a job. Any job, just to get off this ruddy roundabout. Monday to Monday, she lived, pay out day to pay out day.

Might as well go to bed. Tomorrow was another day to get through. She'd sit down and plan out her money for next week. If she was extra careful she could put by that £1 for paint, and it was Martha's day to come over for a cup of tea in the morning. That's if she wasn't too hungover. After the weekend, if she had money, Martha would bring Dave a present and Marie a proper pack of fags. That would really be something to look forward to, that, and a good old gossip. She giggled. Martha would probably know the latest about Lousy Lil and her lodger.

Getting into bed she curled into a ball until she got warm.

A cry came from the cot and then a hearty yell. She crawled out, heaved Dave out of his cot and into her bed. Cuddling him close she whispered, 'Shut up you little bugger or I'll belt you.'

Valerie Thornton

PEARS

It's easy to succeed
with honest-skinned bananas:
it's pears I need to crack.

Dad was good, slicing off dripping discs
between a fine silver blade and his big thumb
for me, for him, for me, for him,

but now they glare for green weeks
from my fruit platter
braced against scent or give

them I bin them
but not before knifing them
just to be sure.

Sometimes they sneak beyond ripe
overnight, it seems, then slobber
fermented, through my fingers.

Avocados darken to their stone hearts,
varicose brown veins, white fur in the clefts,
so far from their green-fingered Aztecs.

But once two pears were,
for a moment, perfect;
a picnic in the car alone at Carrick Castle.

Sweet Red William, black olives in oil and herbs,
white feta and uniformly khaki avocado
spooned in slippery crescents

while the storm swept
down the windscreen
obliterating my world and its ruined keep.

So, shall we dare to half
this last pear? We can split it
between us. Easy.

And if it's wasted
we may yet salvage a drop
to sweeten the lean times ahead.

Gael Turnbull

(from New South Wales, 1852)
THOUGH I HAVE MET WITH HARDSHIP

This is a most beautiful country, all green
to the very tops of the hills, where we arrived
after a good passage but not a quick one,
98 days sailing and then three weeks in quarantine.
Seven persons died on the voyage, two with consumption,
and about 40 of the children, including
I am sorry to relate to you, our youngest lassie, Janet.

Though we had plenty of water and good victuals,
there were too many aboard, 950 emigrants as well as 60 crew,
and a great number took the ship fever. I was very poorly.
Nobody that has got any serious trouble about them
need think they will stand this voyage and I would not advise
any man to come out by the Government ships with a weak famil
because of the want of room and foul air, but it was the cold
and bowel complaint that destroyed all the children.

I work here as a shepherd, well pleased with my master
and if I keep my health, will serve him for the year.
I get £50 and that is the least wage that is going,
and my wife and I soon expect to be independent.
I am very sorry the way shepherds and labourers
are used in Scotland, how little they are thought on.
I would not take a bad word from my master here.
If I should leave him or were sent away,
I would soon get another place and the farmers know that.

Every word I put here is true
as I have got to meet with death, and so, dear brother,
I hope you will make up your mind to come,
you and Donald Macleod and John, the sooner the better,
before your family gets any more in number, for children
are a great trouble and sadness on the voyage.

Give my love to our mother if she is still alive
and tell her that we are as well off as she would wish
though I have met with hardship since I left,
and that I will send her what will do her good
if I be alive for another year, and give our kind love
to all our friends and acquaintances and to Donald Mackay
of Arscaig and his family and I wish they were here
and not on the black muir of Arscaig.

(adapted from an original letter to her great grandfather, in
the possession of Joan Michael of Ullapool)

Brian Whittingham

THE BALANCE OF POWER

The American Mosquito;
A *dipterous* insect

the female has a long *proboscis*
adapted for piercing
the skin of man and animals
to **suck their blood.**

The Scottish Midge;
A *dipterous* insect

A wee fuckin nyaff
that buzzes aboot yir napper
bitin an nibblin wee bits oot yir skin
an generally hee-haw good tae anybody.

Footnote: A government source today revealed that now
Scotland has gained its independence, the Scottish Air Force
Elite (*SAFE*) has placed an order for its first batch of long-
range strategic fighters (*the Midge F 121*). The source stated
this progressive development is crucial in Scotland playing its
part in maintaining the required balance of peace throughout
the Western world. At time of going to press, details of *'project*
Midge' are under wraps. The source did, however, release some
information on the Scottishness of the specification.

1. The *'Midge'* will not carry any conventional weaponry (i.e.
   cannons, missiles, etc.)
2. Instead newly developed 'state of the Scottish art' firepower
   will be introduced.
3. In essence, the effect of this new firepower will result in it
   being a right fucking pest – it will constantly annoy, leaving
   little red blotches on the victim's skin – primarily on the
   arms, face and legs.
4. Prototype testing has shown this aircraft will be particularly
   effective on military, camping beside water and cooking
   smashed potatoes on Aluminium World War 2 cooking
   utensils.

5. We can reveal, however, testing has also shown that smoking
   candles can cause havoc with the aircraft's radar system
   (technicians are working round the clock to eliminate this
   glitch).
6. And finally, all aircraft will have, a dour face complaining
   about the weather, painted on the aircraft's nose and for
   every victorious strike, a transfer of Harry Lauder will be
   stuck on the plane's side.

The government source concluded that *'Midge' squadrons* will
ensure Scotland's role in **NATO's** peacekeeping process and
that Scotland can, and will be, a major player in maintaining
the appropriate balance of power.

Hamish Whyte

ARRAN SEVENS

A derelict blue tractor
    submerges in bracken and
        grass by the side of the String.

The travelling people now
    have provided for them a
        permanent site at Merkland.

A notice in the chemist's
    shop at Whiting Bay says: Free
        transport for cancer patients.

At Thundergay the shearer
    nudges wool from the still sheep:
        the stuff collects in a drift.

DANTE IN GLASGOW

Some shouted:
'Why hold on?'
Some shouted:
'Why let go?'
as the 58
to Mount Blow
bounced
up Hope Street.

Jim C. Wilson

RETIRED

Damned hot again today. Must have a gin,
then check the stocks and shares while Daisy gets
her hair and nails done. There's quite a lot
to do today, in truth. The pears are ripe,
too ripe, almost; (work there for the gardener).
The club, Cedric says, has got a new chef:
Brown Windsor, Gammon Steak and Sunday Roast.
We'll have to check that out; early days, though, yet.
I'll drive to town this afternoon, perhaps;
drop into The Bull for a chinwag,
or watch the golf – a boon that cable set-up.
And the pool could do with a bit of a clean.
So glad we upped our roots and got away.
Life's great. But, God, the Costa's hot today.

DEATH IN VENICE

Von Aschenbach thinks as the tide comes in,
'This is not the Ganges delta.' His lips
close round a strawberry. (It's *such* a sin,
that luscious, dead-ripe fruit.) He sees the hips,
the milky skin of Tadzio. That boy
is perfect classical grace: Greek ideal,
a thing one might aspire to. Oh, what joy
to wait, to watch. And is such beauty real?
In dark back streets, a hot wind stifles. Stone
is sluiced down with disinfectant. A man
is observed; he's powdered and rouged. Alone
he returns to the sand, refines his plan.
Close by his chair a tiger waits to spring.
The tide goes out, a woman starts to sing.

Ross Wilson

DEID?

They say am deid. Deid a' tell ye. Me! Dode fuckin Sharpe deid! A' heard thum speakin last night, the nurses like. 'Nae pulse' they said, 'Nae pulse, he's deid.' Fuckin deid, ah dunno likes, seems hard tae take in.

A' tell ye somehin mate this bein deid caper is nae fuckin joke. Fir a' still hiv thoughts, ken? It's is if, like, ma minds still alive inside ma deid boady. So a' wiz hinkin thit mibe am a spirit noo, ken? Waitin oan the big man upstairs tae whisk ez awo. Mibe am in purgatory, the place where loast souls gan till the big man decides what tae day wy thum... Wether they go up the escalator or doon the lift. A hope he decides soon fir like a sais its nae joke bein a corpse.

When they fund oot that a hid kicked it they pit mi in this room. Thir mustnae be onay central heatin cause it's bloody cauld in here.

A day passes then these cunts come tae confirm it. It is official. Am deid. I'm still no convinced though cause like a kin still think ken, n' dream, n' well deid folk cannae day that cause well thir fuckin deid, eh. Bit I'll no complain I'll jist sit this misconception oot n' wait oan the big man.

Some braw nurses washed mi doon the day. At least a hope it wis braw nurses, that's what a like tae think, cause like well a cannae see, eh. Of course it could hiv been some fuckin stiffy shaggin pervert wy hairy hands n' bad b.o. Bit the braw nurses is a better idea so that's what I'll think. N' by the way a cannae emphasize anuff the fuckin misery o' bein deid is. The fuckin boredom is unbaleivable, n' the wy they treat ye is a fuckin distrace, ye'd hink a wiz apeice o' shite. Ye ken what the cunts dun tae my the day? the bastards. They didnae gan in plug ma ivery orifice, eh. Nae kiddin. They started oaf jist washin ez like, which wiz fair enuff. Bit then jesus fuckin christ they didnae start shuvvin aw these wee plugs intae ez, eh. BASTARDS! In the ears, up the nose, EVEN UP MA FUCKIN ERSE!'... they say a leak! Leak a tell ye. AWO TAE FUCK!a wantid tae tell thum. Git that cork oot o' ma fuckin erse, awo tae fuck. Bit it's nae gid. They couldnae hear ez. Tell ye somehin though mate a didnae half gy wan e' they young nurses a fright. Fir when she pushed me up intae a sittin position (so as they could wash ma

back) ah fuckin grunted! Grunted ah tell ye, right n' er pus an
aw. Even a wiz shoacked. Well this wee nurse hing jist jumps
back n screams, 'He's alive. He breathed. He's alive.' like that
Doctir Frankenstein cunt. N' there's me tryin tae grunt again, tae
confirm it like, tryin tae shout it the cunt a wiz. 'FUCKIN
RIGHT. NOO UNPLUG MA BUM N' BY ME MA LEVIS'. Bit
it wiz nae gid they couldnae hear ez, eh. An aulder nurse telt the
young een thit am no alive eftir aw, that it wis jist the last breath
she heard. When aw the gas in yer stomach presses the gither n
shoots oot the bodies mooth like a fart, or words tae that effect.
A must admit a wiz a bit pissed oaff wy the clarification.

Well of coarse some cunt hud tae identify ez, eh. N' who
better thin ma auld mum. N a'l tell ye she didnae half make
some fuss. 'Aw ma wee boay, ma perr wee boay.' Fuckin
greetin aw er the shoap, she wiz. 'Why ma wee Donald, why
god why?' IT'S DODE. NOO FUCK OFF! A'l tell ye mae thirs
nuthin worse thin cairryin oan like that roond a corpse. What
wid folk hink eh? What aboot ma pride? A might be deid tae
them, tae the ootside world bit ave still goat feelins doon here
ye ken. 'Oh Donald', GIT AWO TAE FUCK YA DAFT AULD
CUNT! Thank fuck ma faither hud the gid sense tae escort her
oot afore she brought eternal shame tae ma life in the eftir
world, if indeed that's where a' am. Cause fuck know's what
this gigs aw aboot likes.

Apparently a wiz killed by a chip. Murdered by a fuckin
chip, kin ye beleive it? They say a chocked oan it, n' cowped er
in the high street, jist like that. Of coarse a wiz half pished it the
time likes. Bought a bag eh chips oan the wy hame fae the pub
n' that, eh. A mustav half swallied the bastard when it lodged in
ma throat. A' loast consciousness n' sconed ma heid aff the kirb.
N' that wiz me endy fuckinstory. Deid, jist like that.

It's been a week noo n' ave been transferred again. It's a
weeir room this time, n fact am convinced that its a fuckin
coffin. A'l tell ye, a hope the big man isnae much loner in takin'
ez up the stairs, cause a kin feel hings in here wy mi. Wee crawly
hings, n' a hink thir hungry.

NOTES ON CONTRIBUTORS

Ken Angus is a semi-retired veterinary pathologist. Publications include papers in various scientific journals and chapters in specialised books. Spare-time poet, having self-published two booklets of verse, *Scotch-potch* and *Eechtie-peechtie-pandy*. Has had several poems accepted for publication in current poetry magazines. 'Airlig Revisited' – finalist in Scottish International Open Poetry Competition 1996.

Meg Bateman was born in Edinburgh in 1959. Publications include *Orain Ghaoil/Amhrain Ghra* (Coisceim) and *Aotromachd agus dain eile* (Polygon). She currently teaches in the Celtic Studies Department at Aberdeen University.

Paul Brownsey was a newspaper reporter after leaving school. He now teaches philosophy at Glasgow University and lives in Bearsden with his partner, Jim McKenzie. His stories have been published in a number of magazines and anthologies, including *Cutting Teeth* and *Flamingo Scottish Short Stories* (Harper Collins, 1995).

Larry Butler is a Californian in Glasgow since 1981, raising two sons, teaching tai-chi, improvising, performing. He works for Survivors' Poetry Scotland organising workshops, performances and publications; published a booklet with Gerry Loose and Kate Sweeney McGee – *Yuga Night* (Writer's Forum), wrote a verse adaptation of Beowulf for the National Theatre, and a scatter of poems here and there.

Stewart Conn, poet and playwright, was born in Glasgow in 1936, brought up in Kilmarnock and now lives in Edinburgh. Most recent poetry: *The Luncheon of the Boating Party* (1992) and *In the Blood* (1995, both Bloodaxe Books) and *at the Aviary* (Snailpress, Cape Town 1995). Co-edited the Shore Poets anthology *The Ice Horses* (Scottish Cultural Press, 1996).

Katrina Crosbie was born and brought up in Glasgow but now lives in Edinburgh with her husband and young son. She is currently working as a freelance journalist, in order to finance her growing obsession with fiction writing. 'No Splash' is her first published short story.

Anne Donovan lives and teaches in Glasgow. Short stories published in *New Writing Scotland 14*, *A Braw Brew* and the *Flamingo Book of New Scottish Writing 1997*. Winner of the *Macallan/Scotland on Sunday* short story competition 1997. Writes mainly, though not exclusively, in Scots.

Moira Duff lives in Aberdeen. Her poetry has been published by *The Rialto, Other Poetry, Smith's Knoll*, the BBC, and this summer one of her poems was on a poster at the new Museum of Scotland. Her novel, *The Vocation of Pearl Duncan*, was published by The Women's Press.

Bill Duncan was born in Fife in 1953 and lives in Dundee. He has had non-fiction, poetry and prose published in *Cencrastus, Chapman, Northwards* and *Full Strength Angels* (New Writing Scotland 14).

Gerrie Fellows lives in Glasgow with her English husband, Scots-born daughter and two passports. *The Promissory Notes* comes from *The Powerlines*, a book-length sequence exploring her New Zealand childhood and Scottish family background. A previous collection, *Technologies*, was published by Polygon. She was SAC Writing Fellow in Paisley 1993–95.

Raymond Friel was born in Greenock in 1963. *Seeing the River*, his first full-length collection of poetry is published by Polygon. He is co-editor of the cultural review, *Southfields*.

Robin Fulton's latest translations include *Five Swedish Poets* (Norvik Press, 1997) and Tomas Transtr̈omer, *New Collected Poems* (Bloodaxe Books, 1997). A book-length selection of his own poems was published in Swedish translation last year and smaller selections are forthcoming in German, Hebrew and Spanish.

Harvey Holton was born in Galashiels in 1949 and now lives in N.E. Fife. He is at home writing having returned from a two month research trip to the USA after spending two years as Writing Fellow for Dundee District Libraries and a year as writer in residence for Dumfries and Galloway Arts Association.

W.N. Herbert is a poet who now lives in Newcastle upon Tyne. He writes both in English and Scots. His latest collection is *Cabaret McGonagall* (Bloodaxe Books, 1996).

A.B. Jackson was born in Glasgow in 1965.

Nasim Marie Jafry was born in 1963 and studied French and English at Glasgow University. She has lived in London and San Francisco and now lives in Edinburgh where she works as a volunteer on a national help-line. She is recovering from ME. Previous stories have appeared in *New Writing Scotland, Northwards* and *Writing Women.*

Brian Johnstone was born in Edinburgh but has lived in Fife since 1969. Published as student; only writing again since mid '80s. Widely published in anthologies and periodicals; first collection, *The Lizard Silence* (Scottish Cultural Press, 1997). Founder of Edinburgh's *Shore Poets.* Readings around Scotland and in Greece; frequent collaborative work with artists and musicians.

Murdo 'Stal' MacDonald was born in 1969 on the Island of Lewis – an arcane Gaelic landscape from which he has drawn much inspiration. He has recently completed a Gaelic Studies degree at Aberdeen University, and lives in the city with his wife Cath and daughter Daisy – the inspiration for 'Faoisgneadh'.

Ciara MacLaverty was born in Belfast in 1968 but has lived in Scotland since childhood. She attended Islay High School and went on to study Arts and Social Sciences at Glasgow University. Previous stories have appeared in *Cutting Teeth* and *West Coast Magazine.* She now lives in Glasgow.

Maureen Macnaughtan is a Glaswegian who has lived in and out of Scotland due to service life. A graduate of Aberdeen University, she currently works as a tutor with Community Education in Fife. First collection, *Kuala Lumpur Traffic,* was published in March 1997 (National Poetry Foundation). Poems in various anthologies.

Aonghas MacNeacail was born on the Isle of Skye in 1942. He is a poet, broadcaster, scriptwriter, journalist and playwright, who writes in Gaelic and English.

Kevin MacNeil was born and raised on the Isle of Lewis and educated at the Nicolson Institute, University of Edinburgh and Sabhal Mòr Ostaig. He was awarded the Logie-Robertson Memorial Award for Scottish Literature whilst at University. MacNeil's writings – poetry and prose – have been widely published, sometimes under his Gaelic name, Caoimhin MacNèill, and sometimes under a pseudonym. Recipient of a Scottish Arts Council Writer's Bursary 1996/97.

John Scott MacPherson/Ian Mac a' Phearsain was born and raised on the Canadian prairie. His mother's people are from Skye, his father's from Islay, and he has been trying to speak Gaelic all of his life. He taught French immersion in high school and made a TV documentary on South Uist emigrants. Presently living in Skye.

Eve Lilith MacRae was born in Edinburgh in 1972, where she lived most of her life. She is now 25, a widow, mother of twins (age 3) and lives in voluntary exile in the Highlands.

John Maley was born in Glasgow in 1962. His poetry has appeared in NWS 9, 10 and 11. Plays for CAT – a theatre company – include *Witch Doctor, Greenock* and *Central and Daylight Robbery.* Films include *High-land Skag and Shortbread* and *All that Glitters.*

Brian McCabe is a poet and fiction writer. Publications include *One Atom to Another* (Polygon), *The Lipstick Circus* (Mainstream), The *Other McCoy* (Mainstream/Penguin), and *In a Dark Room with a Stranger* (Hamish Hamilton/ Penguin).

J. Derrick McClure is a Senior Lecturer in English at Aberdeen University. Author of *Why Scots Matters* (Saltire Society monograph), *Scots and its Literature* (volume of essays), *Scotland o Gael an Lawlander* (Scots translations from contemporary Gaelic poetry) and numerous articles on Scottish linguistic and literary topics. Monograph *Language, Poetry and Nationhood* forthcoming from Tuckwell Press.

Ian McDonough, poet and short story writer, is originally from Brora, Sutherland, and now living and working (as a community mediator) in Edinburgh. Previously published in a wide range of publications including *Chapman, Northwards, The Scotsman* and *Spectrum*. Currently convenor of Edinburgh's Shore Poets.

James McGonigal was born in 1947 and has taught English in schools and colleges in Dumfriesshire and Glasgow. His publications include poetry and short stories in Scots and English, literary and educational studies, and classroom resources. He was co-editor of *New Writing Scotland 12–14* and of *Sons of Ezra: British Poets and Ezra Pound* (1995).

Hugh McMillan lives and works in Dumfries. Publications include *Tramontana* (Dog & Bone), *Horridge* (Chapman), *Aphrodite's Anorak* (Peterloo).

Gordon Meade was former Writing Fellow at Duncan of Jordanstone College of Art and Writer in Residence for Dundee District Libraries (1993/95). Most recent collection, *The Scrimshaw Sailor* (Chapman, 1996). British Council Reading Tour of Belgium and Germany (January 1997). Lives in the East Neuk of Fife with Wilma and their daughter, Sophie.

Gus Morrison was born in Angel Ward, Dumbarton. He served his apprenticeship in Anderson and is now an FE teacher. He is happily married to Kathy and writes when he can.

Michael Munro was born in Glasgow in 1954. He works as freelance editor and lexicographer. Stories and poems in various anthologies and magazines. Play and story broadcast on Radio Scotland. Author of *The Patter – another blast* (Canongate, 1988), *The Complete Patter* (Canongate, 1996) and *The Crack* (Canongate, 1996).

Joe Murray is a self-employed editor, publisher, typesetter and designer. Co-founder of *West Coast Magazine*; co-founder/former editor *Taranis Books*; founder *Mythic Horse Press*. Published in various magazines, journals, newspapers and anthologies. Broadcast: *The Craft of Bookmaking* for Radio Scotland's *Postscript*. Written and directed various commercial and training films.

William Neill (Uilleam Neill) was born in 1922 in Monkton-of-Prestwick, Ayrshire and educated at Ayr Academy, University of Edinburgh. Writer in Gaelic, Scots and English. Several verse collections, translations, essays, radio and TV broadcasts.

David Nicol was born in Dundee in 1962. He has lived in Halifax, Umtata, Dunblane, Edinburgh, Nicaragua, and Glasgow. Some of his poetry has appeared in *West Coast Magazine*, under the pseudonym Alexander Hepburn. He now lives in Aberdeen, where he is writing a novel.

Liz Niven was born in Glasgow in 1952. She is currently teaching and writing in Galloway and was D&G Scots Language Development Officer in 1992–96. Publications include *A Braw Brew* ed., *Solway Stills* ed., *The Tartan Chador other essays* ed. Poetry and prose in *New Writing Scotland, West Coast, Gairfish, Lines Review, Chapman*, BBC Radio, *Skinklin Star*. SAC Bursary 1996.

Martin Osler was born in Dunfermline in 1974 and went to school in Glasgow, Inverness and Knox Academy, Haddington. A Politics and Philosophy graduate from Durham University, he spent a post graduate year at Valdosta State University, Georgia and works as a journalist with the East Lothian Courier.

Tom Pow's latest book of poems is *Red Letter Day* (Bloodaxe). He was Scottish/ Canadian Exchange Writer in 1992–93. A recent SAC Bursary has enabled him to spend time travelling in Africa.

Richard Price's fourth poetry collection, *Hand-held* is published by Akros. He co-edits the little magazine *Southfields* with David Kinloch and Raymond Friel and works in London at the British Library as a Curator of Modern British Collections.

Sheila Puri is a 38 year old Asian Glaswegian. She has two children and works as a counsellor for a women's organisation. She is a member of Southside Writers group.

Cynthia Rogerson was born in 1953; American, grew up near San Francisco. Travelled to Canada, Mexico, United States, Europe, finally settled in Rosshire twenty years ago. Many jobs, all odd. Married, four children. Stories and poems published in *Northwards 1, 2* and *12; Boundaries, Second Thoughts, Third Edition, Faultlines, Heron, The Broadsheet*. Twice finalist Neil Gunn Competition.

Kamaljit Sangha was born in London and now lives in Glasgow. He has had stories published in *Critical Quarterly* and *Cutting Teeth*. He is working on his first collection.

Hamid Shami was born in Pakistan and bred in Glasgow, where he now lives.

Iain Crichton Smith was born in 1928 – poet, novelist and short story writer. Best known novel is *Consider the Lilies*. Has published *Collected Poems* and most recent book is *The Human Face*.

Ian Stephen was born in 1955 on the Isle of Lewis. Author of many books of poems, most recently *Broad Bay* (Morning Star Publications). Awards include Christian Salvesen/RLS fellowship; two Scottish Arts Council bursaries and a new public work for An Tobar, Mull. Runs Writing Centre in Benside, Lewis.

Jean Tarras has lived in Banff for thirty years where she works as a part-time locum pharmacist and has three grown-up children.

Valerie Thornton writes poems and short stories. Her first poetry collection is being published by Scottish Cultural Press. She was short-listed for the Macallan/SoS short story prize in 1992, and her Scottish creative writing anthology, *Working Words*, was TESS/Saltire Society Education Book of the Year in 1996.

Gael Turnbull's most recent publications include *For Whose Delight* (Mariscat) and *To the Tune of Annie Lawrie* (Akros).

Brian Whittingham is a poet whose publications include *Swiss Watches & the Ballroom Dancer* (Taranis) and *Industrial Deafness* (Crazy Day Press). He is poetry editor of *West Coast Magazine*.

Hamish Whyte lives and works in Glasgow. He has published two collections of poems and edited several anthologies, including *The Scottish Cat, Mungo's Tongues: Glasgow Poems 1630–1990* and recently, *An Arran Anthology*. He is currently trying to translate bits of Martial.

Jim C. Wilson was born in Edinburgh and started writing at 33. He was Writing Fellow for Stirling District (1989–1991). A prose work, *The Happy Land* (Ramsay Head Press), was a Radio Scotland series. His most recent poetry collection is *Cellos in Hell* (Chapman). In 1997 he won the Hugh MacDiarmid Trophy.

Ross Wilson is 18 years old and lives in Kelty, Fife. He is a member of Lochgelly's 'Nearly Famous' writers group.